REGISTERED TRADEMARK

FOURIER ANALYSIS

Alan D. Solomon, Ph.D.

Research and Education Association
61 Ethel Road West
Piscataway, New Jersey 08854

THE ESSENTIALS OF
FOURIER ANALYSIS ®

Printed in the United States of America

Library of Congress Catalog Card Number 89-62091

International Standard Book Number 0-87891-697-0

ESSENTIALS is a registered trademark of
Research and Education Association, Piscataway, New Jersey 08854

WHAT "THE ESSENTIALS" WILL DO FOR YOU

This book is a review and study guide. It is comprehensive and it is concise.

It helps in preparing for exams, in doing homework, and remains a handy reference source at all times.

It condenses the vast amount of detail characteristic of the subject matter and summarizes the **essentials** of the field.

It will thus save hours of study and preparation time.

The book provides quick access to the important facts, principles, theorems, concepts, and equations in the field.

Materials needed for exams can be reviewed in summary form – eliminating the need to read and re-read many pages of textbook and class notes. The summaries will even tend to bring detail to mind that had been previously read or noted.

This "ESSENTIALS" book has been prepared by an expert in the field, and has been carefully reviewed to assure accuracy and maximum usefulness.

Dr. Max Fogiel
Program Director

CONTENTS

CHAPTER 1

PERIODIC FUNCTIONS

One of the great successes of modern mathematical analysis was the recognition that signals, or functions representing signals, could be decomposed into combinations of pure sine and cosine waves with various frequencies. In familiar terms this means that signals such as those recognized as speech, the noise of motors and other machines or the beating of our hearts, could be broken down in terms of periodic **components** with different periods. The field of Fourier Analysis is where this connection is made and studied. The basis for this field is the idea of **periodic function**, which is the subject of this chapter.

1.1 PERIODIC FUNCTIONS

DEFINITION 1.1: PERIODIC FUNCTION

A function $f(t)$ is **periodic** if for all t

$$f(t) = f(t + T) \tag{1.1}$$

for some value T.

REMARK 1.1

Relation (1.1) implies that for all natural numbers $n = 1, 2, \ldots,$

$$f(t) = f(t \pm nT) \qquad (1.2)$$

DEFINITION 1.2:   PERIOD OF A PERIODIC FUNCTION

The value T of (1.1) is referred to as the **period** of the function f.

EXAMPLE 1.1

The function $f(t) = \sin(t)$ is periodic with period 2π. Similarly, $\cos(2t)$ is periodic with period π since

$$\cos(2t) = \cos(2(t + \pi))$$

for all t.

DEFINITION 1.3:   HARMONIC VIBRATION

A **harmonic vibration** is a function of the form

$$f(t) = A \sin[\omega t - \delta] \qquad (1.3a)$$

or

$$f(t) = A \cos[\omega t - \delta] \qquad (1.3b)$$

where A, δ, ω are arbitrary real numbers, and A, $\omega > 0$.

DEFINITION 1.4:   AMPLITUDE OF A HARMONIC VIBRATION

The number A of (1.3a,b) is the **amplitude** of the corresponding harmonic wave.

DEFINITION 1.5:   CIRCULAR/ANGULAR FREQUENCY:

The value ω of (1.3a,b) is the **circular** or **angular frequency** of the corresponding harmonic wave; this is the number of oscillations or vibrations in time 2π. The harmonic wave

2

is a periodic function with period

$$T = {}^{2\pi}/_{\omega} \qquad\qquad (1.4)$$

since, for example,

$$\sin(\omega t) = \sin[\omega(t - {}^{2\pi}/_{\omega})].$$

The **frequency** is the value $f_0 = {}^{\omega}/_{2\pi}$ (Figure 1.1).

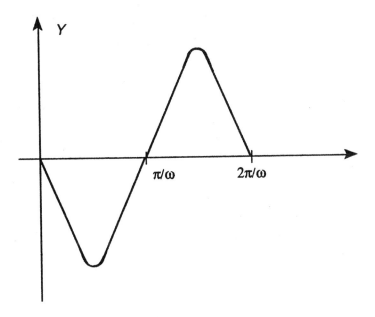

Figure 1.1– $Y = \sin(\omega t)$

REMARK 1.2

For any real numbers a, b and angular frequency ω the function

$$f(t) = a \cos(\omega t) + b \sin(\omega t)$$

is a harmonic wave. For if we define the angle δ by

$$\delta = \arctan\left(^b/_a\right)$$

then the addition formula for the cosine

$$\cos(\alpha + \beta) = \cos(\alpha)\cos(\beta) - \sin(\alpha)\sin(\beta)$$

tells us that

$$f(t) = (a^2 + b^2)^{1/2}\,[\cos(\omega\,t)\cos(\delta) + \sin(\omega\,t)\sin(\delta)]$$

$$= A\cos(\omega\,t - \delta)$$

which is a harmonic wave with amplitude

$$A = [a^2 + b^2]^{1/2}.$$

DEFINITION 1.6: PHASE ANGLE OF A HARMONIC VIBRATION

The angle $\alpha = \omega\,t - \delta$ of the harmonic wave (1.3a, b) is its **phase**. Note that in some books the term "phase angle" is reserved for the phase shift which is defined next.

DEFINITION 1.7: PHASE SHIFT/DISPLACEMENT OF A HARMONIC VIBRATION

The angle δ of the harmonic wave (1.3a, b) is its **phase shift** or **displacement**.

DEFINITION 1.8: LEFT/RIGHT LIMITS OF A FUNCTION AT A POINT

The **left hand** and **right hand** limits of a function $f(t)$ at a point t_0, denoted by $f(t_0 - 0)$ and $f(t_0 + 0)$, respectively, are defined by

$$f(t_0 - 0) = \lim_{t \to t_0, t < t_0} f(t), \qquad (1.5a)$$

4

$$f(t_0 + 0) = \lim_{t \to t_0, t > t_0} f(t). \tag{1.5b}$$

DEFINITION 1.9:   JUMP DISCONTINUITY OF A FUNCTION AT A POINT

A function $f(t)$ with right and left hand limits $f(t_0 + 0)$, $f(t_0 - 0)$ at the point t_0 has a **jump discontinuity** at t_0 if

$$f(t_0 - 0) \neq f(t_0 + 0). \tag{1.6}$$

DEFINITION 1.10: PIECEWISE CONTINUITY OF A FUNCTION

A function $f(t)$ is **piecewise continuous** on an interval $a \leq t \leq b$ if it is continuous at all points of the interval with the possible exception of a finite number of points at which it has a jump discontinuity.

EXAMPLE 1.2

The function $f(t)$ whose graph is shown in Figure 1.2 has jump discontinuities at the points t_0, t_1, t_2, t_3 pictured there.

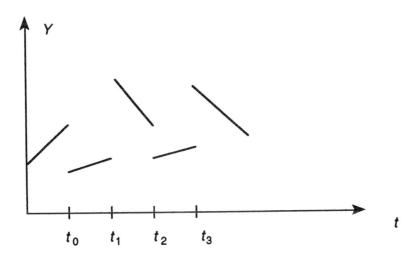

Figure 1.2–A Function with Jump Discontinuities

DEFINITION 1.11: MEAN VALUE AT A JUMP DISCONTINUITY

At a jump discontinuity t_0 the **mean value** of a function $f(t)$ is defined as

$$f^{\text{mean}}(t_0) = \frac{1}{2}[f(t_0 - 0) + f(t_0 + 0)]. \qquad (1.7)$$

1.2 TRIGONOMETRIC POLYNOMIALS AND SUPERPOSITION

DEFINITION 1.12: TRIGONOMETRIC POLYNOMIALS

A **trigonometric polynomial of order N** is a function of the form

$$S_N(t) = \frac{1}{2}a_0 + \sum_{n=1}^{N} (a_n \cos(n\omega t) + b_n \sin(n\omega t))$$

$$= \frac{1}{2}a_0 + \sum_{n=1}^{N} A_n \cos(n\omega t - \delta_n). \qquad (1.8)$$

EXAMPLE 1.3

The function

$$f(t) = \sin(t) - \frac{1}{2}\sin(2t)$$

is a trigonometric polynomial whose graph is shown in Figure 1.3. The function is periodic with period 2π.

DEFINITION 1.13: SUPERPOSITION OF HARMONIC WAVES

A **superposition** of harmonic waves is a function of the form

$$f(t) = \sum_{n=1}^{N} a_n \cos(\omega_n t - \delta_n) \qquad (1.9)$$

6

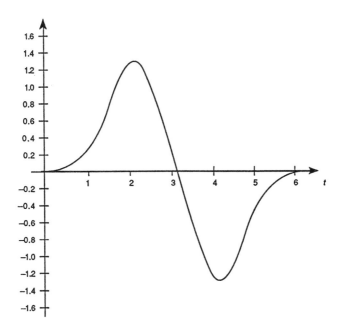

Figure 1.3–The Function $Y = f(t) = \sin(t) - \frac{1}{2}\sin(2t)$

where the angular frequencies (ω_n) form an increasing sequence of real numbers,

$$0 < \omega_1 < \omega_2 < \ldots$$

The sum in (1.9) may be finite (N finite) or infinite ($N = \infty$), assuming convergence in the latter case.

DEFINITION 1.14: FUNDAMENTAL AND HIGHER HARMONICS

If the angular frequencies ω_n in the superposition of harmonic waves (1.9) are all integer multiples of the first angular frequency,

$$\omega_n = n\omega_1$$

then we refer to the wave $\cos(\omega_1 t - \delta_1)$ as the **first** or **fundamental harmonic**; the angular frequency ω_1 is the **fundamen-**

7

tal angular frequency. The harmonics $\cos(\omega_2 t - \delta_2)$, $\cos(\omega_3 - \delta_3)$, ..., $\cos(\omega_n - \delta_n)$ are the **second, third, ... nth harmonics**, respectively, while their angular frequencies ω_2, ω_3, ..., ω_n are the **second, third, nth** harmonic angular frequencies. The corresponding frequencies (**not** angular!) are $\omega_1/2\pi$, $\omega_2/2\pi$, ..., $\omega_n/2\pi$ and are referred to as the **fundamental, second, ..., nth** harmonic frequencies.

EXAMPLE 1.4

In the superposition of harmonics

$$f(t) = \sin(t) - \sin(3t) + \tfrac{1}{2}\sin(16t)$$

the fundamental harmonic is $\sin(t)$; the third harmonic is $-\sin(3t)$; the 16th is $\tfrac{1}{2}\sin(16t)$.

DEFINITION 1.15: BEATS

Beats are rhythmic changes of amplitude arising in superpositions of harmonics from the interaction of the superposed functions.

EXAMPLE 1.5

The function

$$f(t) = \sin(t) + \sin(3t)$$

may be rewritten as

$$f(t) = 2\cos(t)\sin(2t).$$

To see this we simply note that

$$\sin(3t) = \sin(2t + t)$$

$$= \sin(2t)\cos(t) + \sin(t)\cos(2t)$$

so that

8

$$f(t) = \sin(t) + \sin(t) \cos(2t) + \sin(2t) \cos(t)$$

$$= \sin(t)[1 + \cos(2t)] + \sin(2t) \cos(t).$$

But by the relation $\cos(2t) = \cos^2(t) - \sin^2(t)$ we have

$$1 + \cos(2t) = 1 - \sin^2(t) + \cos^2(t)$$

$$= 2 \cos^2(t)$$

so that

$$f(t) = 2 \cos^2(t) \sin(t) + \sin(2t) \cos(t)$$

$$= \sin(2t) \cos(t) + \sin(2t) \cos(t)$$

$$= 2 \sin(2t) \cos(t)$$

where we have used the sine relation

$$\sin(2t) = 2 \sin(t) \cos(t).$$

The function $2 \sin(2t) \cos(t)$ represents the harmonic $\cos(t)$ multiplied by the "amplitude" $2 \sin(2t)$ which vanishes for $t = 0$, $\pi/2$, π, $3\pi/2$, π. The time-varying "amplitude" of the wave is of a higher frequency than the harmonic.

DEFINITION 1.16: WAVE FUNCTION SYMMETRIES

Harmonic waves may have various kinds of symmetries. Some key symmetries are the following:

EVEN FUNCTION
$$f(t) = f(-t) \text{ for all } t \text{ (Figure 1.4).}$$

ODD FUNCTION
$$f(t) = -f(-t) \text{ for all } t \text{ (Figure 1.5).}$$

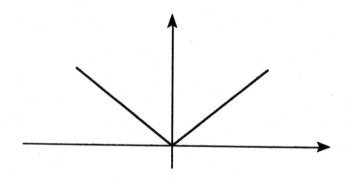

Figure 1.4–An Even Function

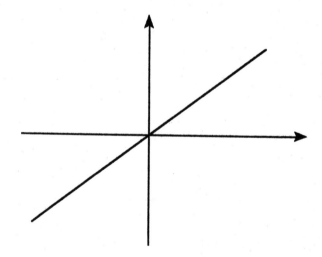

Figure 1.5–An Odd Function

For a periodic function $f(t)$ with period T:

10

HALF-WAVE SYMMETRIC

$f(t) = -f(t + \frac{1}{2} T)$ for all t (Figure 1.6).

EVEN QUARTER-WAVE SYMMETRIC

$f(t)$ is half-wave symmetric and even (Figure 1.7).

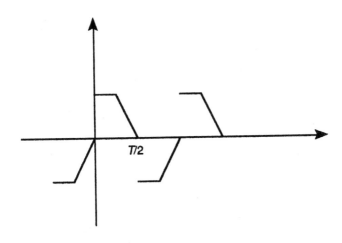

Figure 1.6–Half-Wave Symmetry

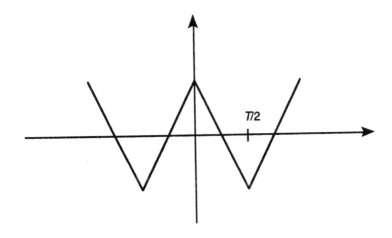

Figure 1.7–Even Quarter-Wave Symmetry

11

ODD QUARTER-WAVE SYMMETRIC

$f(t)$ is half-wave symmetric and odd (Figure 1.8).

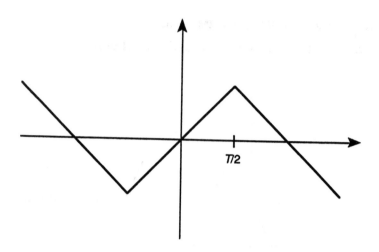

Figure 1.8–Odd Quarter-Wave Symmetry

1.3 COMPLEX NOTATION

By Euler's formula from the field of Complex Variables we know that for any z,

$$e^{iz} = \cos(z) + i\sin(z),$$

$$e^{-iz} = \cos(z) - i\sin(z).$$

Adding these relations and dividing by 2 gives us

$$\cos(z) = {}^1\!/_2\,(e^{iz} + e^{-iz})$$

while subtraction and division by 2i (using $1/i = -i$) yields

$$\sin(z) = -{}^1\!/_2 i\,(e^{iz} - e^{-iz}).$$

12

Replacing the trigonometric functions by the exponentials in the relation (1.9) for harmonic wave superpositions will give us expressions of the form

$$f(t) = \sum_{n=-N}^{N} B_n \exp(i\omega_n t) \qquad (1.10)$$

where the sum is over both positive and negative integers n.

DEFINITION 1.17: COMPLEX WAVE SUPERPOSITION

A general **complex wave superposition** is a function of the form

$$f(t) = \sum_{n=-N}^{N} B_n \exp(i\omega_n t)$$

where the numbers B_n may be complex, and the ω_n are the wave frequencies.

EXAMPLE 1.6

The harmonic superposition

$$f(t) = \cos(t) - 3\cos(2t)$$

can be rewritten in the form

$$f(t) = \tfrac{1}{2}(e^{it} + e^{-it}) - (\tfrac{3}{2})(e^{2it} + e^{-2it}).$$

CHAPTER 2

FOURIER SERIES

The aim of Fourier Analysis is to establish a connection between a function and its decomposition into elemental pure harmonic waves. It is remarkable that this can be done for a huge variety of functions, including not only periodic functions but many discontinuous functions and functions vanishing outside of some finite interval.

We now formalize this connection by means of the **Fourier series representation** of a function as an infinite sum of harmonic waves. In one step this representation gives us two rewards: the relationship between a function and its elemental harmonic waves (the subject of this chapter) and a representation, like that of the Taylor series, that provides us with simple analytical approximations (in Chapter 3).

2.1 THE CONCEPT OF FOURIER SERIES

DEFINITION 2.1: FOURIER SERIES EXPANSION OF A
CONTINUOUS FUNCTION ON THE INTERVAL
$-\pi < x < \pi$

The **Fourier Series expansion** of a continuous function $f(t)$ on the interval $-\pi < x < \pi$ is given by the infinite sum

$$f(t) = \tfrac{1}{2}a_0 + \sum_{n=1}^{\infty} [a_n \cos(nt) + b_n \sin(nt)] \qquad (2.1)$$

where the coefficients a_n, b_n are defined as

$$a_n = (1/\pi) \int_{-\pi}^{\pi} f(s)\cos(ns)ds \qquad (2.2)$$

$$b_n = (1/\pi) \int_{-\pi}^{\pi} f(s)\sin(ns)ds. \qquad (2.3)$$

DEFINITION 2.2:   FOURIER COEFFICIENTS

The coefficients a_n, b_n are the **Fourier coefficients** of $f(t)$.

DEFINITION 2.3:   FOURIER SERIES ON THE INTERVAL
$$-L < t < L$$

As in (2.1) the **Fourier series expansion** of a continuous function $f(t)$ on the interval $-L < t < L$ is given by

$$f(t) = \tfrac{1}{2}a_0 + \sum_{n=1}^{\infty} [a_n \cos(n\pi t/L) + b_n \sin(n\pi t/L)] \quad (2.4)$$

where the coefficients a_n, b_n are

$$a_n = (1/L) \int_{-L}^{L} f(s)\cos(n\pi s/L)ds \qquad (2.5)$$

$$b_n = (1/L) \int_{-L}^{L} f(s)\sin(n\pi s/L)ds \qquad (2.6)$$

for $n = 0, 1, 2, \ldots.$ If $f(t)$ is periodic with period $T = 2L$, then in terms of the angular frequency

$$\omega_0 = 2\pi/T = \pi/L$$

the Fourier series (2.4) takes the form

$$f(t) = \frac{a_0}{2} + \sum_{n=1}^{\infty} [a_n \cos(\omega_0 nt) + b_n \sin(\omega_0 nt)] \quad (2.7)$$

and the Fourier coefficients are given by

$$a_n = (2/T) \int_{-T/2}^{T/2} f(t) \cos(n\omega_0 t) dt \quad (2.8)$$

$$b_n = (2/T) \int_{-T/2}^{T/2} f(t) \sin(n\omega_0 t) dt. \quad (2.9)$$

DEFINITION 2.4: DIRICHLET CONDITIONS FOR CONVERGENCE:

$f(t)$ satisfies the **Dirichlet Conditions** if

a) it is periodic with period $2L$;

b) it is differentiable everywhere on the interval $-L \le t \le L$ except at a finite number of points;

c) $f(t)$ and $f'(t)$ are piecewise continuous on $[-L, L]$;

d) at points of discontinuity $f(t)$ is defined by its mean value.

REMARK 2.1

We sometimes say that a function $f(t)$ is **piecewise smooth** if it satisfies the Dirichlet conditions.

REMARK 2.2: MANNERS OF CONVERGENCE

The infinite series

$$\sum_{n=0}^{\infty} f_n(t) \quad (2.10)$$

converges in a **pointwise manner** to the function $f(t)$ on the interval $a \leq t \leq b$ if for any point t^* on the interval the following condition holds: given any $\varepsilon > 0$ there is a natural number N, depending possibly on ε and t^*,

$$N = N(\varepsilon, t^*) \qquad (2.11)$$

such that all partial sums of (2.10) of at least N terms

$$S_m(t) = \sum_{n=0}^{N} f_n(t), \quad (\text{for } m > N) \qquad (2.12)$$

are closer to $f(t^*)$ than ε at t^*:

$$| S_m(t^*) - f(t^*) | < \varepsilon. \qquad (2.13)$$

We say that the series converges **uniformly** to $f(t)$ on $a \leq t \leq b$ if the number N of (2.11) can be chosen independently of t^*; that is, given any ε there is an $N = N(\varepsilon)$ dependent only on ε, such that

$$| S_m(t) - f(t) | < \varepsilon \qquad (2.14)$$

for all $m > N$.

THEOREM 2.1:   FUNDAMENTAL CONVERGENCE THEOREM FOR FOURIER SERIES

If $f(t)$ satisfies the Dirichlet conditions then the Fourier Series (2.4) converges to $f(t)$ at every point of continuity of the function; at a point of discontinuity, convergence is to the mean value of f. Convergence is **pointwise**. On any closed interval $a \leq t \leq b$ in which $f(t)$ is continuous, convergence is uniform.

EXAMPLE 2.1

Let $f(t)$ be periodic with period 2π, and defined on the interval $-\pi \leq t \leq \pi$ as (Figure 2.1)

$$f(t) = t^2.$$

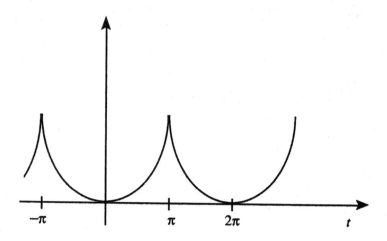

Figure 2.1– $Y = f(T)$**: The Even Periodic Extension**
of $f(t) = t$

Then $f(t)$ satisfies the Dirichlet conditions and in addition is continuous everywhere; therefore convergence of its Fourier series is uniform. To find its Fourier coefficients we substitute $f(t)$ into the relations (2.4-2.6). Firstly, all the b_n, defined by

$$b_n = (1/\pi) \int_{-\pi}^{\pi} t^2 \sin(nt)\,dt \qquad (2.15)$$

are equal to zero. To see this we may write b_n as the sum of two integrals, over $-\pi < t < 0$ and over $0 < t < \pi$,

$$b_n = (1/\pi) \int_{-\pi}^{0} t^2 \sin(nt)\,dt + (1/\pi) \int_{0}^{\pi} t^2 \sin(nt)\,dt$$

If we introduce the variable $s = -t$ in the first integral we find $ds = -dt$, $t = -s$ and $\sin(-ns) = -\sin(ns)$ so that

18

$$(1/\pi) \int_{-\pi}^{0} t^2 \sin(nt)\,dt = -(1/\pi) \int_{\pi}^{0} (-s)^2 \sin(-ns)\,ds$$

$$= -(1/\pi) \int_{0}^{\pi} s^2 \sin(ns)\,ds$$

and since s is simply a "dummy variable" we can rename it "t", giving us

$$b_n = -(1/\pi) \int_{0}^{\pi} t^2 \sin(nt)\,dt + \int_{0}^{\pi} t^2 \sin(nt)\,dt$$

$$= 0.$$

This result is clear on geometrical grounds. For the integrand of (2.15) is an **odd function**,

$$(-t)^2 \sin(-nt) = -t^2 \sin(nt)$$

so that its graph is asymmetric with respect to $t = 0$. Therefore its areas on the intervals $[-\pi, 0]$ and $[0, \pi]$ cancel. The coefficients a_n are given by

$$a_n = (1/\pi) \int_{-\pi}^{\pi} t^2 \cos(nt).$$

For $n = 0$,

$$a_n = (1/\pi) \int_{-\pi}^{\pi} t^2\,dt = 2\pi^2/3.$$

Using integration by parts we find, for $n > 0$,

$$a_n = (1/n\pi)\,(t^2 \sin(nt))\big|_{-\pi}^{\pi} - (2/n\pi) \int_{-\pi}^{\pi} t \sin(nt)\,dt$$

The first term vanishes. The integral can again be integrated by parts, giving us

$$a_n = (2/n^2\pi)\,[t \cos(nt)]\big|_{-\pi}^{\pi} - (2/\pi n^2) \int_{-\pi}^{\pi} \cos(nt)\,dt$$

The integral is zero, while the first term gives us

$$a_n = (4 / n^2) \cos(n\pi) = (-1)^n (4 / n^2).$$

Therefore the function $f(t)$ has the Fourier series expansion

$$f(t) = \pi^2/3 - 4[\cos(t) - (1/2^2) \cos(2t)$$

$$+ (1/3^2) \cos(3t) + - \ldots].$$

THEOREM 2.2: GIBBS PHENOMENON

In any interval $a \leq t \leq b$ containing a point of discontinuity of $f(t)$, the convergence of the partial sums of the Fourier series

$$S_N(t) = a_0/2 + \sum_{n=1}^{N} [a_n \cos(nt) + b_n \sin(nt)] \quad (2.16)$$

to $f(t)$ is pointwise and not uniform. Unlike the non-uniform convergence of the sequence t_n to the function that "jumps" from 0 to 1 at $t = 1$, the non-uniform convergence of the partial sums $S_N(t)$ of (2.16) to $f(t)$ is marked by an "overshooting" of $f(t)$ near the point of discontinuity by about 9%. This is known as **Gibbs phenomenon.**

THEOREM 2.3: RIEMANN-LEBESQUE THEOREM

For any function $f(t)$ satisfying the Dirichlet conditions, on any interval $a < t < b$,

$$\lim_{n \to \infty} \int_a^b f(t)\cos(nt)\,dt = \lim_{n \to \infty} \int_a^b f(t)\sin(nt)\,dt$$

$$= 0$$

THEOREM 2.4: BESSEL'S INEQUALITY

For any piecewise continuous function $f(t)$ (not necessarily satisfying the Dirichlet conditions), if we define the Fourier coefficients a_n, b_n by (2.5, 6) then

$$\frac{1}{2}a_0^2 + \sum_{n=1}^{\infty} [a_n^2 + b_n^2] \le (1/L) \int_{-L}^{L} (f(t))^2 dt \qquad (2.17)$$

THEOREM 2.5: PARSEVAL'S IDENTITY

If $f(t)$ satisfies the Dirichlet conditions then Bessel's inequality is an equality in the limit for $N \to \infty$,

$$\frac{1}{2}a_0^2 + \sum_{n=1}^{\infty} [a_n^2 + b_n^2] = (1/L) \int_{-L}^{L} (f(t))^2 dt. \qquad (2.18)$$

DEFINITION 2.5: FOURIER SERIES REPRESENTATION USING COMPLEX NOTATION

Using complex notation the Fourier series representation assumes the form

$$f(t) = \sum_{n=-\infty}^{\infty} \alpha_n e^{in\pi t/L} \qquad (2.19)$$

with the Fourier coefficients α_n defined by

$$\alpha_n = (1/2L) \int_{-L}^{L} f(t) e^{-in\pi t/L} dt. \qquad (2.20)$$

REMARK 2.3

If we write

$$\alpha_n = \Gamma_n e^{i\delta_n} \qquad (2.21)$$

where $\Gamma_n = |\alpha_n|$ while δ_n is the argument of α_n, and if we set $\omega_0 = \pi/L$, then (2.19) becomes

21

$$f(t) = \sum_{n=-\infty}^{\infty} \Gamma_n \, \exp[i(n\omega_0 t + \delta_n)] \qquad (2.22)$$

where ω_0 is the fundamental angular frequency and δ_n is the displacement of the nth harmonic. The values Γ_n are referred to as the **discrete spectrum** of f. These values describe the influence of the various harmonics of frequencies $n \, \omega_0$ and the displacements δ_n as they combine to form the function $f(t)$.

DEFINITION 2.6: FEJER ARITHMETIC MEANS, FOR A FUNCTION SERIES

Let S_N be the Nth partial sum of the Fourier series expansion for $f(t)$, given by (2.16). Then the **Fejer arithmetic mean** of the Fourier series is defined by

$$\Omega_N(t) = (1/[N + 1]) \, [S_0(t) + S_1(t) + \ldots + S_N(t)] \qquad (2.23)$$

THEOREM 2.6: FEJER'S THEOREM

If $f(t)$ is periodic and continuous then the Fejer arithmetic mean $\Omega_N(t)$ converges uniformly to $f(t)$ for $N \to \infty$. At points of piecewise discontinuity the Fejer arithmetic means **do not** exhibit the Gibbs phenomenon.

2.2 FOURIER SERIES IN SPECIAL CASES

THEOREM 2.7: FOURIER SERIES FOR FUNCTIONS OF SPECIAL WAVE FORMS

Considerations similar to those used to prove the vanishing of the Fourier coefficients b_n of the even function t^2 of Example 2.1 are used to prove similar statements for functions having the kinds of symmetry of Definition 1.16. In particular we can show the following:

a) **EVEN FUNCTIONS:** If $f(t)$ is an even periodic function with period T, $f(t) = f(-t)$, then its Fourier series consists of cosine terms only:

$$f(t) = a_0 + \sum_{n=1}^{\infty} a_n \cos(n\omega_0 t)$$

with the angular frequency $\omega_0 = 2\pi / T$ and the Fourier coefficients

$$a_n = (2/T) \int_{-T/2}^{T/2} f(t)\cos(n\omega_0 t)dt$$

$$= (4/T) \int_{0}^{T/2} f(t)\cos(n\omega_0 t)dt.$$

b) **ODD FUNCTIONS:** If $f(t)$ is periodic with period T and odd, $f(t) = -f(-t)$, then its Fourier series consists only of sine terms,

$$f(t) = \sum_{n=1}^{\infty} b_n \sin(n\omega_0 t) \qquad (2.24)$$

where the Fourier coefficients are given by

$$b_n = (2/T) \int_{-T/2}^{T/2} f(t)\sin(n\omega_0 t)dt$$

$$= (4/T) \int_{0}^{T/2} f(t)\sin(n\omega_0 t)dt. \qquad (2.25)$$

c) **HALF-WAVE SYMMETRIC FUNCTIONS:** Half-wave symmetry of $f(t)$ means (See Definition 1.16) that $f(t)$ is periodic with period T and obeys $f(t) = -f(t + \frac{1}{2} T)$. The Fourier series of half-wave symmetric functions contains only odd order harmonics with the Fourier coefficients

$$a_n = \begin{cases} 0, & \text{for even } n \\ (4/T) \int_0^{T/2} f(t)\cos(n\omega_0 t)dt, \\ & \text{for odd } n, \end{cases} \qquad (2.26)$$

$$b_n = \begin{cases} 0, & \text{for even } n \\ (4/T) \int_0^{T/2} f(t)\sin(n\omega_0 t)dt, \\ & \text{for odd } n, \end{cases} \qquad (2.27)$$

with the fundamental angular frequency $\omega_0 = 2\pi / T$. The Fourier series of $f(t)$ takes the form

$$f(t) = \sum_{n=0}^{\infty} [a_{2n+1}\cos((2n+1)\omega_0 t) + b_{2n+1}\sin((2n+1)\omega_0 t)]. \qquad (2.28)$$

d) **EVEN/ODD QUARTER-WAVE SYMMETRIC FUNC-TIONS**: These are half-wave symmetric period functions that in addition are even or odd, respectively. If $f(t)$ is even, then the b_n are all zero while the a_n are given by

$$a_n = (8/T)\int_0^{T/4} f(t)\cos(n\omega_0 t)dt.$$

If $f(t)$ is odd, then the a_n are all zero while the b_n are given by

$$b_n = (8/T) \int_0^{T/4} f(t) \sin(n\omega_0 t) dt.$$

THEOREM 2.8: EXTENSIONS OF A FUNCTION DEFINED ON A FINITE INTERVAL

A function $\phi(t)$ defined on a finite interval $a < t < b$ may be assigned a **periodic extension** $f(t)$ which exhibits any of the given wave forms of Definition 1.16 and coincides with $\phi(t)$ on $a < t < b$.

THEOREM 2.9: FOURIER SERIES EXPANSIONS FOR A FUNCTION DEFINED ON A FINITE INTERVAL

If $\phi(t)$ is a function which together with its derivative is defined and piecewise continuous on an interval $a < t < b$, then it admits of alternative Fourier series expansions according as it is extended periodically with any of the wave forms of Definition 1.16.

EXAMPLE 2.2

Let $\phi(t)$ be defined as

$$\phi(t) = 1, \quad 0 < t < 1.$$

Then an EVEN periodic extension $f_1(t)$ of $\phi(t)$ is provided by the function

$$f_1(t) \equiv 1, -\infty < t < \infty,$$

having the trivial Fourier series expansion $a_0 = 1$, $a_n = b_n = 0$, $n \neq 0$.

An ODD periodic extension $f_2(t)$ of ϕ is given by

$$f_2(t) = \begin{cases} 1, & 0 < t < 1 \\ -1, & -1 < t < 0 \end{cases}$$

and

$$f_2(t) = f_2(t + 2)$$

where period $T = 2$. In this case the Fourier coefficients are given by (2.25) with fundamental frequency $\omega_0 = 2\pi / T = \pi$. Since f_2 is odd, the Fourier coefficients a_n all vanish, while the b_n are

$$b_n = (4/T) \int_0^{T/2} f_2(t)\sin(n\omega_0 t)dt$$

$$= 2 \int_0^2 \sin(n\pi t)dt$$

$$= -(2/n\pi)\cos(n\pi t)\Big|_0^2$$

$$= \begin{cases} 0, & \text{for even } n \\ 4/n\pi, & \text{for odd } n \end{cases}$$

so that the Fourier series of $f_2(t)$ is finally

$$f_2(t) = (4/\pi) \sum_{n=0}^{\infty} [\sin((2n + 1)\pi t)]/(2n + 1) \quad (2.29)$$

Note that in addition to being odd and periodic, $f_2(t)$ is also half-wave symmetric, since

$$f_2(t) = -f_2(t + 1)$$

that is,

$$f_2(t) = -f(t + \tfrac{1}{2}T).$$

2.3   MULTIDIMENSIONAL FOURIER SERIES

The results of Sections 2.1, 2.2 carry over for functions of two or more variables. The form of the Fourier Series for a function of two independent variables is given by the next theorem for a function which is periodic in each of its variables with period 2π.

THEOREM 2.10: FOURIER SERIES FOR A FUNCTION OF TWO VARIABLES

Let D denote the region

$$D: -\pi \leq s \leq \pi, \quad -\pi \leq t \leq \pi. \qquad (2.30)$$

Let $f(s, t)$ be piecewise continuous and periodic with period 2π with respect to each of its variables: i.e. $f(s + 2m\pi, t + 2n\pi) = f(s, t)$, $m, n = 0, \pm 1, \pm 2, \ldots$. Then $f(s, t)$ may be expanded in a **double Fourier series** given by

$$
\begin{aligned}
f(s,t) = \sum_{m=0}^{\infty} \sum_{n=0}^{\infty} \tau_{mn} \{ &a_{mn} \cos(ms) \cos(nt) \\
&+ b_{mn} \sin(ms) \cos(nt) + c_{mn} \cos(ms) \sin(nt) \\
&+ d_{mn} \sin(ms) \sin(nt) \}
\end{aligned}
\qquad (2.31)
$$

where

$$
\tau_{mn} = \begin{cases}
1/4, & \text{for } m = n = 0 \\
1/2, & \text{for } m > 0, n = 0 \text{ or } n > 0, m = 0 \\
1, & \text{for } m, n > 0
\end{cases}
\qquad (2.32)
$$

and the **Fourier coefficients** a_{mn}, b_{mn}, c_{mn}, d_{mn} are given by the integrals:

27

$$a_{mn} = (1/\pi^2) \int\int_D f(s,t) \cos(ms) \cos(nt) \, ds \, dt \qquad (2.33)$$

$$b_{mn} = (1/\pi^2) \int\int_D f(s,t) \sin(ms) \cos(nt) \, ds \, dt \qquad (2.34)$$

$$c_{mn} = (1/\pi^2) \int\int_D f(s,t) \cos(ms) \sin(nt) \, ds \, dt \qquad (2.35)$$

$$d_{mn} = (1/\pi^2) \int\int_D f(s,t) \sin(ms) \sin(nt) \, ds \, dt \qquad (2.36)$$

In **complex terms** this Fourier Series takes the form

$$f(s,t) = \sum_{m=-\infty}^{\infty} \sum_{n=-\infty}^{\infty} \alpha_{mn} e^{1(ms+nt)} \qquad (2.37)$$

where the complex Fourier coefficients α_{mn} are given by

$$\alpha_{mn} = (1/4\pi^2) \int\int_D f(s,t) \, e^{-1(ms+nt)} \, ds \, dt. \qquad (2.38)$$

THEOREM 2.11: BESSEL'S INEQUALITY FOR FUNCTIONS OF TWO VARIABLES

The Fourier coefficients (2.33-36) of $f(s,t)$ satisfy **Bessel's Inequality**,

$$\sum_{m=-\infty}^{\infty} \sum_{n=-\infty}^{\infty} \tau_{mn}[a_{mn}^2 + b_{mn}^2 + c_{mn}^2 + d_{mn}^2]$$

$$\leq (1/4\pi^2) \int\int_D f(s,t)^2 \, ds \, dt \qquad (2.39)$$

In the complex form (2.37) Bessel's inequality becomes

$$\sum_{m=-\infty}^{\infty} \sum_{n=-\infty}^{\infty} |\alpha_{mn}|^2 \leq (1/4\pi^2) \iint_D f(s,t)^2 ds \, dt. \quad (2.40)$$

2.4 DIFFERENTIATION AND INTEGRATION OF FOURIER SERIES

THEOREM 2.12: TERMWISE INTEGRATION OF A FOURIER SERIES

Let $f(t)$ satisfy the Dirichlet conditions and have the Fourier Series representation

$$f(t) = \tfrac{1}{2}a_0 + \sum_{n=1}^{\infty} [a_n \cos(n\omega_0 t) + b_n \sin(n\omega_0 t)] \quad (2.41)$$

with fundamental angular frequency ω_0 and Fourier coefficients a_n, b_n. Then over any interval $a < t < b$ the integral of $f(t)$ is equal to the series obtained by term-by-term integration of (2.41):

$$\int_a^b f(t) \, dt = \tfrac{1}{2}a_0(b-a) + \sum_{n=1}^{\infty} [a_n \int_a^b \cos(n\omega_0 t) \, dt$$

$$+ b_n \int_a^b \sin(n\omega_0 t) dt] \quad (2.42)$$

with of course

$$\int_a^b \cos(n\omega_0 t) \, dt = (1/n\omega_0) \{\sin(n\omega_0 b) - \sin(n\omega_0 a)\}$$

$$\int_a^b \sin(n\omega_0 t) \, dt = -(1/n\omega_0) \{\cos(n\omega_0 b) - \cos(n\omega_0 a)\}$$

EXAMPLE 2.3

As we have seen in Example 2.2, the Fourier Series expansion of the function $f(t)$ defined as

$$f(t) = \begin{cases} -1, & \text{for } -1 < t \le 0 \\ 1, & \text{for } 0 \le t < 1 \end{cases}$$

is

$$f(t) = (4/\pi) \sum_{n=0}^{\infty} (1/(2n+1)) \sin[(2n+1)\pi t] \quad (2.43)$$

If

$$g(t) = |t| \text{ on } -1 < t < 1$$

then

$$f(t) = g'(t),$$

or

$$g(t) = \int_0^t f(s)\,ds, \text{ for } -1 < t < 1$$

and $g(t)$ may be found by integrating the Fourier series (2.43) term-by-term: in particular, taking the interval from $t = {}^1/_2$ to any general point t on $(-1, 1)$ gives us

$$g(t) - \tfrac{1}{2} = (4/\pi) \sum_{n=0}^{\infty} (1/(2n+1)) \int_{1/2}^t \sin((2n+1)\pi s)\,ds$$

or

$$g(t) = \tfrac{1}{2} - (4/\pi^2) \sum_{n=0}^{\infty} [1/(2n+1)^2] \cos((2n+1)\pi t)$$

where we have made use of the vanishing of $\cos((2n+1)\pi t)$ for $t = {}^1/_2$.

THEOREM 2.13: TERMWISE DIFFERENTIATION OF A FOURIER SERIES

Let $f(t)$ be a function satisfying the Dirichlet conditions and having the Fourier Series expansion (2.41). Then the Fourier Series expansion of the derivative of $f'(t)$ can be obtained from that for $f(t)$ by term-by-term differentiation:

$$f'(t) = \omega_o \sum_{n=1}^{\infty} n[-a_n \sin(n\omega_0 t) + b_n \cos(n\omega_0 t)] \quad (2.44)$$

CHAPTER 3

FOURIER SERIES AND VECTOR SPACE CONCEPTS

The idea of a "Vector Space" is an extension of the familiar concept of a "vector" in two or three dimensions. Thus in two dimensions we refer to an ordered pair of numbers $\mathbf{u} = (x_1, x_2)$ as a "vector" – an entity having the **direction** determined by the line from the origin to the point (x, y), and the **magnitude** or **norm** given by the length of this line,

$$\| \mathbf{u} \| = [x_1^2 + x_2^2]^{1/2}.$$

Vectors can be **multiplied** by numbers, according to the rule that if $\mathbf{u} = (x_1, x_2)$ then for any real number a

$$a\mathbf{u} = (ax_1, ax_2)$$

and **added,** according to the rule that if $\mathbf{u} = (x_1, x_2)$ and $\mathbf{v} = (y_1, y_2)$ then

$$\mathbf{u} + \mathbf{v} = (x_1 + y_1, x_2 + y_2).$$

In addition, vectors may be multiplied in two ways: a) the **inner** or **dot** product, and b) the **vector** product. The inner product of two vectors, which is of key interest to us in Fourier

Analysis, is defined as follows: if $\mathbf{u} = (x_1, x_2)$ and $\mathbf{v} = (y_1, y_2)$ then their inner product is the number

$$(\mathbf{u}, \mathbf{v}) = x_1 y_1 + x_2 y_2.$$

In addition the inner product is equal to

$$(\mathbf{u}, \mathbf{v}) = \|\mathbf{u}\| \cdot \|\mathbf{v}\| \cos(\theta)$$

where θ is the angle between the two vectors. Thus the two vectors $\mathbf{u}$, $\mathbf{v}$ are **orthogonal** if the angle θ is equal to $90°$, that is,

$$(\mathbf{u}, \mathbf{v}) = 0. \tag{3.1}$$

The subject of **linear algebra** is based on the fact that these ideas can be generalized in such a way that we can describe geometric concepts in analytical terms for spaces not only of two and three dimensions but for "general" n-dimensional spaces as well. Thus in N space dimensions a **vector** is an ordered sequence of N numbers

$$\mathbf{u} = (x_1, x_2, \ldots, x_N)$$

such that multiplication by a real number (or "scalar") a is defined by

$$a\mathbf{u} = (ax_1, ax_2, \ldots, ax_N);$$

addition of two vectors

$$\mathbf{u} = (x_1, x_2, \ldots, x_N)$$

$$\mathbf{v} = (y_1, y_2, \ldots, y_N)$$

is defined by

$$\mathbf{u} + \mathbf{v} = (x_1 + y_1, x_2 + y_2, \ldots, x_N + y_N)$$

33

while their inner product is given by

$$(\mathbf{u}, \mathbf{v}) = \sum_{n=1}^{N} x_n y_n.$$

The **norm** or **magnitude** of the vector **u** is defined as

$$\| \mathbf{u} \| = \{(\mathbf{u}, \mathbf{v})\}^{1/2} = \left\{ \sum_{n=1}^{N} x_n^{\,2} \right\}^{1/2}.$$

With this we obtain the **Cauchy-Schwarz-Bunyakovski** (CSB) inequality, according to which

$$| (\mathbf{u}, \mathbf{v}) | \leq \| \mathbf{u} \| \cdot \| \mathbf{v} \| \tag{3.2}$$

with equality holding if and only if **u** is a scalar multiple of **v**, and **u** = a**v** for some real number v. On the basis of the CSB inequality we may define the angle θ between the vectors **u**, **v** of N-dimensional space by the relation

$$\cos(\theta) = (\mathbf{u}, \mathbf{v}) / [\| \mathbf{u} \| \cdot \| \mathbf{v} \|] \tag{3.3}$$

thus extending the 2-dimensional relation to N-dimensional space. In particular, equation 3.3 makes it possible for us to speak of angles, directions and geometry in N-dimensions. Thus, for example, two vectors **u** and **v** are orthogonal if their inner product is zero:

$$(\mathbf{u}, \mathbf{v}) = 0. \tag{3.4}$$

In this chapter we look at Fourier Series from a point of view based on extending the ideas of vectors from finite sequences of N numbers defining N-dimensional space, to functions in a space of infinitely many dimensions.

DEFINITION 3.1: CONTINUOUS FUNCTIONS AS VECTORS

Let $a \leq t \leq b$ be any interval on the real line, and let Ω be the collection of all piecewise continuous functions $f(t)$ having piecewise continuous derivatives on the interval. If we multiply any such function by a real number we obtain yet another function in Ω,

$$g(t) = af(t)$$

while the sum of two such functions is also another function in Ω

$$g(t) = f_1(t) + f_2(t).$$

Thus we say that Ω **is closed** under multiplication by real numbers and addition. In particular, any **linear combination** of two functions $f_1(t), f_2(t)$, defined as

$$g(t) = a_1 f_1(t) + a_2 f_2(t),$$

is also in Ω. The set Ω also contains a "zero" vector, namely the function identically vanishing on the interval $[a, b]$.

DEFINITION 3.2: LINEAR COMBINATION OF FUNCTIONS

A **linear combination** of functions $f_1, f_2, \ldots, f_M$ is a function of the form

$$g(t) = \sum_{n=1}^{M} a_n f_n(t) \qquad (3.5)$$

for real constants $a_1, a_2, \ldots, a_M$.

DEFINITION 3.3: INNER PRODUCT OF CONTINUOUS FUNCTIONS

We define the **inner product** of two functions $f_1(t), f_2(t)$ in Ω as the integral of their product over the interval $[a, b]$,

$$(f_1, f_2) = \int_a^b f_1(t) f_2(t) dt. \qquad (3.6)$$

This inner product obeys all the formal rules obeyed by the inner product in 2, 3, or N-dimensions. In particular, the inner product of a function with itself is always positive, vanishing only for the function that identically vanishes in the interval:

$$(f_1, f_1) > 0, \quad = 0 \text{ if and only if } f_1(t) \equiv 0. \tag{3.7}$$

EXAMPLE 3.1

If $f_1(t) = t, f_2(t) = t^2$ on $[0,1]$ then

$$(f_1, f_2) = \int_0^1 f_1(t) f_2(t) dt = 1/4.$$

DEFINITION 3.4:   NORM OF A FUNCTION

We define the **norm** $||f_1||$ of a function $f_1(t)$, as in the case of an N-dimensional vector, by the relation

$$||f_1|| = \{(f_1, f_1)\}^{1/2}$$

$$= \left\{ \int_a^b f_1(t)^2 \, dt \right\}^{1/2}.$$

THEOREM 3.1:   CAUCHY-SCHWARZ-BUNYAKOVSKI (CSB) INEQUALITY

For any functions f_1, f_2,

$$|(f_1, f_2)| \leq ||f_1|| \cdot ||f_2|| \tag{3.8}$$

with equality holding only if f_1 is a constant multiple of f_2, $f_1 = af_2$, or vice-versa.

DEFINITION 3.5:   ANGLE BETWEEN FUNCTIONS

We define the **angle** θ between the functions f_1, f_2 of Ω by the relation

$$\cos(\theta) = (f_1, f_2) / [\|f_1\| \cdot \|f_2\|]$$ (3.9)

By the CSB inequality the ratio on the right-hand side always lies between -1 and 1, so that an angle θ can always be found. Similarly, if

$$f_1 = af_2$$

for some positive number a, then the ratio on the right is 1, the cosine is zero and $\theta = 0$, corresponding to the expected result that the functions should then be "parallel." If on the other hand $a < 0$, then the ratio would be equal to -1, the angle θ would be equal to $180°$ and the functions would be "pointing" in "opposite directions" as expected.

DEFINITION 3.6:   ORTHOGONALITY OF FUNCTIONS

Two functions f_1 and f_2 are **orthogonal** if their inner product is zero,

$$(f_1, f_2) = 0.$$

Of course, this corresponds to the vanishing of the cosine of (3.9).

THEOREM 3.2:   ORTHOGONALITY OF THE TRIGONOMETRIC FUNCTIONS

The trigonometric functions **sin, cos** obey particularly important orthogonality relations when considered on the interval $-\pi \le t \le \pi$. The following relations hold:

A)   For any natural numbers m, n the functions $\sin(mt)$ and $\cos(nt)$ are orthogonal:

$$\int_{-\pi}^{\pi} \sin(mt) \cos(nt)\, dt = 0, \quad m, n = 0, 1, 2,....$$ (3.10)

37

B) For any natural numbers $m \neq n$, the functions $\cos(mt)$ and $\cos(nt)$ are orthogonal. Generally

$$\int_{-\pi}^{\pi} \cos(mt)\cos(nt)\,dt = \begin{cases} 0, & \text{for } m \neq n \\ \pi, & \text{for } m = n > 0 \\ 2\pi, & \text{for } m = n = 0. \end{cases} \quad (3.11)$$

C) For any natural numbers $m \neq n$, the functions $\sin(mt)$ and $\sin(nt)$ are orthogonal. Generally

$$\int_{-\pi}^{\pi} \sin(mt)\sin(nt)\,dt = \begin{cases} 0, & \text{for } m \neq n \\ \pi, & \text{for } m = n. \end{cases} \quad (3.12)$$

DEFINITION 3.7:   ORTHONORMALITY OF FUNCTIONS

The functions f_1, f_2 are **orthonormal** if they are orthogonal and their norms are both equal to 1. More generally, an **orthonormal set of functions** is a set of functions which are mutually orthogonal and of unit norm.

REMARK 3.1

For any function $f(t)$ with norm $||f||$, the function $g(t)$ defined as

$$g(t) = f(t) / ||f||$$

has norm 1,

$$||g|| = 1.$$

DEFINITION 3.8:   LINEAR INDEPENDENCE/DEPENDENCE

A pair of functions f_1, f_2 is **linearly independent** if neither can be expressed as the product of the other by a constant. Alternatively, they are linearly independent if the angle between them is neither 0 nor 180°. A collection of M functions, $f_1, f_2, \ldots, f_M$ is **linearly independent** if it is not possible to represent any one of them as a linear combination of the others. On the other hand, the functions are **linearly dependent** if at least one of them can be expressed as a linear combination of the remaining functions.

EXAMPLE 3.2

The functions $\cos(t)$ and $\cos(2t)$ are linearly independent, since $\cos(t)$ vanishes for $t = \pi/2$ while $\cos(2t)$ does not. Similarly for any natural number M the collection of functions 1, $\cos(t)$, $\cos(2t)$, ..., $\cos(Mt)$, $\sin(t)$, $\sin(2t)$, ..., $\sin(Mt)$ is linearly independent.

THEOREM 3.3: GRAM-SCHMIDT ORTHOGONALIZATION PROCEDURE

The Gram-Schmidt orthogonalization procedure is a procedure by which we obtain a collection of mutually orthogonal functions or vectors from a linearly independent collection. The procedure is best explained by an example.

EXAMPLE 3.3: GENERATING A MUTUALLY ORTHOGONAL SET OF FUNCTIONS FROM THE FUNCTIONS 1, t, t² ON THE UNIT INTERVAL

We begin by setting $f_1(t) \equiv 1$. Let

$$f_2(t) = t - \alpha f_1(t)$$

for some number α which is yet to be determined. We will seek a value α that forces f_1 and f_2 to be orthogonal. This means that

$$0 = (f_1, f_2) = \int_0^1 1 \cdot [t - \alpha] dt$$

$$= 1/2 - \alpha$$

That is, we chose $\alpha = 1/2$ and

$$f_2(t) = t - \tfrac{1}{2}.$$

We now seek $f_3(t)$ such that it will be orthogonal to both f_1 and f_2, that is, so that the conditions

$$(f_1, f_3) = 0 \qquad\qquad (3.13)$$

and

$$(f_2, f_3) = 0 \qquad\qquad (3.14)$$

are both true. This is done by looking for f_3 in the form of a linear combination of the previously found functions (which are already orthogonal), and t^2. The coefficients of the linear combination are to be determined so that (3.13, 14) hold. Specifically, choose

$$f_3 = t^2 - \alpha f_1 - \beta f_2.$$

Substitution of f_3 into (3.13) and using the orthogonality of f_1 and f_2 gives us

$$0 = \int_0^1 t^2 dt - \alpha,$$

or $\alpha = \tfrac{1}{3}$. Similarly, substitution of f_3 into (3.14) and using the orthogonality of f_1 and f_2 now implies that

$$0 = \int_0^1 t^2(t - 1/2)dt - \beta \int_0^1 (t - 1/2)^2 dt$$

giving us $\beta = 1$, so that

$$f_3(t) = t^2 - (1/3) - (t - 1/2).$$

The functions obtained by the procedure may be **normalized** by dividing them by their norms. In this way we obtain functions having unit norm and orthogonal to each other. For f_1, f_2 and f_3 of our example,

$$\|f_1\| = 1, \quad \|f_2\| = 1/2\sqrt{3}, \quad \|f_3\| = 1/6\sqrt{5}$$

so that the functions

$$\phi_1 = f_1, \quad \phi_2 = 2\sqrt{3}\, f_2, \quad \phi_3 = 6\sqrt{5}\, f_3$$

are orthonormal.

EXAMPLE 3.4

For $m, n = 1, 2, 3, \ldots$, the collection of functions

$$1/\sqrt{2\pi}, \quad (1/\sqrt{\pi})\sin(mt), \quad (1/\sqrt{\pi})\cos(nt)$$

is orthonormal in the sense of the inner product (3.6) on the interval $[-\pi, \pi]$. Each is of norm 1 (by 3.11, 12)) and each is orthogonal to all the others.

DEFINITION 3.9: NEAREST LINEAR COMBINATION OF ORTHONORMAL FUNCTIONS TO A GIVEN FUNCTION

Let (ϕ_n) be an orthonormal collection of N functions, $n = 1, 2, \ldots, N$, and let f be a given function. The **nearest linear combination** of the ϕ_n to f is the linear combination

$$\sum_{n=1}^{N} \alpha_n \phi_n \qquad (3.16)$$

which, over all choices of the coefficients $\{\alpha_n\}$, minimizes the distance

$$E = \left\| f - \sum_{n=1}^{N} \alpha_n \phi_n \right\|. \qquad (3.17)$$

If the norm is measured over an interval $[a, b]$, then finding this linear combination is equivalent to minimizing the **root mean square error**

$$RMS = \left\{ \int_a^b \left[f(t) - \sum_{n=1}^{N} \alpha_n \phi_n(t) \right]^2 dt \right\}^{1/2} . \qquad (3.18)$$

THEOREM 3.4: THE FOURIER APPROXIMATION TO A FUNCTION

The linear combination (3.16) minimizing the root mean square error (3.18) is found by setting

$$\alpha_n = (f, \phi_n)$$

$$= \int_a^b f(t) \phi_n(t) \, dt. \qquad (3.19)$$

With this choice of coefficients the linear combination

$$\sum_{n=1}^{N} \alpha_n \phi_n(t)$$

constitutes the best approximation to f among all such linear combinations in the sense of the root mean square error (3.18).

DEFINITION 3.10: FOURIER COEFFICIENTS

The coefficients α_n of (3.19) are the **Fourier coefficients** of f.

EXAMPLE 3.5

If on the interval $[-\pi, \pi]$ we choose the trigonometric functions of Example 3.4 as our orthonormal set, then the Fourier coefficients are of the form

$$(1/\sqrt{\pi}) \int_{-\pi}^{\pi} f(t) \cos(nt)\, dt$$

$$(1/\sqrt{\pi}) \int_{-\pi}^{\pi} f(t) \sin(nt)\, dt,$$

while the "best linear combination" in the sense of the root mean square error (3.18) will coincide with the Fourier polynomial as defined by (3.16). Note that the "Fourier coefficients" defined by Definitions 2.2, 2.3 have been multiplied by $1/\sqrt{2\pi}$ and $1/\sqrt{\pi}$ for the sake of convenience.

THEOREM 3.5: BESSEL'S INEQUALITY

For the Fourier coefficients α_n of (3.19),

$$\|f\|^2 \geq \sum_{n=1}^{N} \alpha_n{}^2. \qquad (3.20)$$

DEFINITION 3.11: CONVERGENCE IN THE SENSE OF THE ROOT-MEAN SQUARE ERROR

Let $\{\phi_n\}$ be an orthonormal set of infinitely many functions. Moreover, suppose that the sequence of partial sums

$$S_N = \sum_{n=1}^{\infty} \alpha_n \phi_n \qquad (3.21)$$

converges to the function f in the sense of the root mean square error (RMS) tending to zero for $n \to \infty$,

$$\left\| f - \sum_{n=1}^{N} \alpha_n \phi_n \right\| \to 0 \text{ for } N \to \infty. \qquad (3.22)$$

Then we say that the Fourier series

$$\sum_{n=1}^{\infty} \alpha_n \phi_n \qquad (3.23)$$

converges to f in the sense of the root mean square error. This type of convergence is also referred to as "least square" or "L_2" convergence.

DEFINITION 3.12: COMPLETENESS

The orthonormal family $\{\phi_n\}$ is **complete** if there is a linear combination of these functions converging to every function f having a finite norm.

THEOREM 3.6: PARSEVAL'S IDENTITY

If the family $\{\phi_n\}$ is complete, then Bessel's inequality (3.20) can be replaced by equality in the limit for $N \to \infty$:

$$\|f\|^2 = \sum_{n=1}^{\infty} \alpha_n^2. \qquad (3.24)$$

DEFINITION 3.13: WEIGHTED INNER PRODUCTS AND NORMS

All of the above results hold true if we alter the definition (3.6) of the inner product to the form

$$(f,g) = \int_a^b W(t)f(t)\,g(t)\,dt \qquad (3.25)$$

where $W(t) > 0$ is a given continuous function. Such weights are used to "stress" certain regions of the interval $[a, b]$ in relation to others. Of course the norm of a function will now be

$$\|f\| = \left\{ \int_a^b W(t)f(t)^2 dt \right\}^{1/2}. \qquad (3.26)$$

DEFINITION 3.14: INNER PRODUCT AND NORM IN HIGHER DIMENSIONS

If D is a domain in the s, t plane and Ω is a collection of piecewise continuous functions $f(s, t)$, $g(s, t)$, ..., on D, then the **inner product** (f, g) of f and g can be defined as

$$(f,g) = \int \int_D f(s, t)\, g(s, t)\, ds\, dt. \qquad (3.27)$$

Similarly the **norm** of f is

$$\|f\| = \left\{ \int \int_D f(s,t)^2\, ds\, dt \right\}^{1/2}. \qquad (3.28)$$

REMARK 3.2

A derivation of the relation (3.19) for the Fourier coefficients can be based on the relation

$$f(t) = \sum_{n=1}^{\infty} \alpha_n \phi_n(t)$$

assuming convergence of the series. Let m be any natural number and take the inner product of both sides of this equation with ϕ_m. Since ϕ_n is orthogonal to ϕ_m for $n = m$,

$$(\phi_m, \phi_n) = 0.$$

At the same time, since the ϕ_n all have norm 1,

$$(\phi_m, \phi_m) = 1,$$

so that the right-hand side inner product with ϕ_m is equal to α_m. On the left-hand side we obtain the inner product (f, ϕ_m), thus implying that

$$\alpha_m = (f, \phi_m).$$

In defining the Fourier Series expansion with respect to an orthonormal family of functions the only geometric concept needed by us was that of **orthogonality**. We can extend this to **complex valued functions** as follows.

DEFINITION 3.15: THE INNER PRODUCT FOR COMPLEX-VALUED FUNCTIONS

Let $f(t)$ and $g(t)$ be two possibly complex valued functions defined on $a \leq t \leq b$, each of them piecewise continuous with piecewise continuous derivatives. Then the inner product of f and g is

$$(f,g) = \int_a^b f(t)\, \overline{g(t)}\, dt \qquad (3.29)$$

where $\overline{g(t)}$ is the complex conjugate of $g(t)$.

DEFINITION 3.16: NORM OF A FUNCTION

The norm of a function obeying the conditions of Definition 3.15 is defined as

$$\lVert f \rVert = \{(f,f)\}^{1/2}. \qquad (3.30)$$

DEFINITION 3.17: ORTHOGONALITY OF FUNCTIONS

The functions f, g are **orthogonal** if their inner product is zero,

$$(f, g) = 0. \qquad (3.31)$$

DEFINITION 3.18: ORTHONORMAL FAMILY OF FUNCTIONS

A family of functions is **orthonormal** if they are mutually orthogonal and if all have norms equal to 1.

With these definitions all of the earlier results for real valued functions carry over to the complex-valued case.

EXAMPLE 3.6

On the interval $-T/2 \le t \le T/2$, the functions

$$\phi_n(t) = (1/\sqrt{T})\, e^{in\omega_0 t}, \quad n = 0, \pm 1, \ldots$$

with angular frequency $\omega_0 = 2\pi/T$ make up an orthonormal, complete collection; a function $f(t)$ which obeys the Dirichlet conditions can be expanded in a Fourier series with respect to these functions, of the form

$$f(t) = \sum_{n=-\infty}^{\infty} \alpha_n \phi_n(t) \tag{3.32}$$

with the α_n found from (3.19).

DEFINITION 3.19: STURM-LIOUVILLE PROBLEM:

Sturm-Liouville problems are boundary value problems for ordinary differential equations having solutions that constitute complete orthonormal systems of functions. An example is that of the boundary value problem of solving

$$u''(t) = ku(t) \tag{3.33}$$

on the interval $0 \le t \le \pi$, for the boundary conditions

$$u(0) = u(\pi) = 0. \tag{3.34}$$

The Sturm-Liouville problem consists of asking for all possible values of the parameter k (the **eigenvalues**) for which corresponding solutions (the **eigenfunctions**) exist. Clearly if k is of the form

$$k = -m^2, m = 1, 2, \ldots \tag{3.35}$$

47

then the corresponding solution to the boundary value problem exists and is given by

$$u(t) = u_m(t) = \sin(mt). \tag{3.36}$$

Furthermore, for any pair $m, n = 1, 2, \ldots$, if we use the relation

$$\sin(mt) \sin(nt) = \frac{1}{2}\{\cos((m-n)t) - \cos((m+n)t)\}$$

then we see that

$$\int_0^\pi \sin(mt) \sin(nt) = \begin{cases} 0, & \text{for } m \neq n \\ \pi/2, & \text{for } m = n. \end{cases}$$

Therefore the sequence of functions

$$\phi_m(t) = \{2/\pi\}^{1/2} \sin(mt)$$

constitutes an orthonormal family of functions; moreover, ϕ_m is an eigenfunction corresponding to the eigenvalue $-m^2$.

On the basis of the theory of Sturm-Liouville problems we can show that in general the eigenfunctions provide us with a complete orthonormal family of functions which in turn can be used for the Fourier Series expansion of functions.

CHAPTER 4

FOURIER TRANSFORMS

The Fourier Transform is one of the key tools in analyzing information coming from such sources as radar and signals, noise and communication systems. In addition, the transform enables us to solve a variety of problems of mathematical physics. Like the Fourier Series, of which it is a limiting form, it provides a means both for representing functions and for analyzing their behavior.

4.1 FUNDAMENTAL CONCEPTS

DEFINITION 4.1:   ABSOLUTELY INTEGRABLE FUNCTION

Let $f(t)$ be defined and piecewise continuous for all real t. Then $f(t)$ is **absolutely integrable** if the integral

$$\int_{-\infty}^{\infty} |f(t)|\, dt \qquad (4.1)$$

which is defined as the limit

$$\lim_{\substack{A \to -\infty \\ B \to \infty}} \int_{A}^{B} |f(t)|\, dt \qquad (4.2)$$

independent of the manner in which A and B grow, exists.

THEOREM 4.1: THE LIMIT OF THE FOURIER SERIES AS THE PERIOD TENDS TO INFINITY

For any value $T > 0$ suppose that $f(t)$ obeys the Dirichlet conditions on the interval $-\frac{1}{2}T < t \leq \frac{1}{2}T$. Then $f(t)$ can be expanded in the Fourier Series

$$f(t) = a_0/2 + \sum_{n=1}^{\infty} \{a_n \cos(n\omega_0 t) + b_n \sin(n\omega_0 t)\} \quad (4.3)$$

where the angular frequency $\omega_0 = 2\pi/T$. Here the Fourier coefficients are given by

$$a_n = (2/T) \int_{-T/2}^{T/2} f(t) \cos(n\omega_0 t)\, dt \quad (4.4)$$

$$b_n = (2/T) \int_{-T/2}^{T/2} f(t) \sin(n\omega_0 t)\, dt. \quad (4.5)$$

If in these relations we let T grow without limit, $T \to \infty$, then we can show that the equation (4.3) tends to the relation

$$f(t) = (1/\pi) \int_0^{\infty} d\tau \int_{-\infty}^{\infty} f(s) \cos(s - \tau)\, ds \quad (4.6)$$

This formula expresses the **Fourier Integral Theorem.**

THEOREM 4.2: EQUIVALENT FORMS OF THE FOURIER INTEGRAL THEOREM

Equivalent forms of the Fourier Integral theorem (4.6) are

$$f(t) = (1/2\pi) \int_{-\infty}^{\infty} \int_{-\infty}^{\infty} f(\tau) e^{is(t-\tau)}\, d\tau\, ds \quad (4.7)$$

and

$$f(t) = (1/2\pi) \int_{-\infty}^{\infty} e^{ist} ds \int_{-\infty}^{\infty} f(\tau) e^{-is\tau} d\tau. \qquad (4.8)$$

DEFINITION 4.2: FOURIER TRANSFORM

The **Fourier Transform** of a function $f(t)$ is the function $F(s)$ defined as

$$F(s) \int_{-\infty}^{\infty} f(\tau) \exp(-is\tau) d\tau. \qquad (4.9)$$

We will write

$$F = \Phi(f) \quad \text{or} \quad F(\tau) = \Phi\{F\}[\tau] \qquad (4.10)$$

to represent the fact that **F is the Fourier transform** of f. By the Fourier Integral theorem (4.8)

$$f(t) = (1/2\pi) \int_{-\infty}^{\infty} F(s) e^{ist} ds. \qquad (4.11)$$

We say that $f(t)$ and $F(\tau)$ are a **Fourier Transform** pair with $f(t)$ constituting the **inverse Fourier Transform** to $F(\tau)$. This will be represented by the notation

$$f = \Phi^{-1}\{F\} \qquad (4.12)$$

The Fourier Transform is a complex-valued function of τ.

REMARK 4.1

The precise definition of the Fourier Transform varies formally from book to book with regard to where the factor $1/2\pi$ is placed. In some sources the Fourier Transform is defined by multiplying Equation (4.9) by $1/\sqrt{2\pi}$ and (4.11) by $\sqrt{2\pi}$. The Fourier Integral theorem expressed by (4.8) would of course be unchanged. In studying this material from a text the student MUST make certain which definition is being used.

51

THEOREM 4.3: FOURIER TRANSFORMS OF ODD AND EVEN FUNCTIONS

If $f(t)$ is an odd function satisfying the conditions of Theorem 4.1, then the Fourier Integral Formula takes the form

$$f(t) = (2/\pi) \int_0^\infty \left\{ \sin(st) \int_0^\infty f(\tau) \sin(s\tau) dr \right\} ds \quad (4.13)$$

while for even $f(t)$ we obtain

$$f(t) = (2/\pi) \int_0^\infty \left\{ \cos(st) \int_0^\infty f(\tau) \cos(s\tau) dr \right\} ds \quad (4.14)$$

If **for odd f(t)** we define the **FOURIER SINE TRANSFORM** $F_s(\tau)$ by

$$F_S(\tau) = \int_0^\infty f(t)\sin(t\tau) \, dt \quad (4.15)$$

then from (4.13), $f(t)$ is the **inverse** Fourier sine transform of F_s,

$$f(t) = (2/\pi) \int_0^\infty F_s(\tau)\sin(t\tau) \, dr. \quad (4.16)$$

In the same way, if $f(t)$ is **even** and if we define the **FOURIER COSINE TRANSFORM** F_c by

$$F_C(\tau) = \int_0^\infty f(t)\cos(t\tau) \, dt \quad (4.17)$$

then from (4.14), $f(t)$ is the **inverse** Fourier cosine transform of F_c,

$$f(t) = (2/\pi) \int_0^\infty F_C(\tau)\cos(t\tau) \, d\tau. \quad (4.18)$$

EXAMPLE 4.1

Define the function

$$f(t) = \begin{cases} 1, & \text{for } 0 < t < 1 \\ 0, & \text{elsewhere} \end{cases}$$

By direct substitution into (4.9) we find that

$$\Phi\{f\}[S] = (i/s)[e^{-is} - 1].$$

THEOREM 4.4: ELEMENTARY PROPERTIES OF THE FOURIER TRANSFORM

The Fourier transform has the following elementary properties:

A. **Linearity:** The transform of a linear combination of functions is the corresponding linear combination of the transforms:

$$\Phi\{\alpha f_1 + \beta f_2\} = \alpha\Phi\{f_1\} + \beta\Phi\{f_2\} \qquad (4.19)$$

for constants α, β.

B. **Time shifting:** The transform of a function with a delayed argument is equal to the transform of the function rotated through an angle proportional to the delay:

$$\Phi\{f(t - t^*)\} = \Phi(f)\exp(-i\,\tau\,t^*). \qquad (4.20)$$

C. **Frequency shifting:** The inverse transform evaluated at a delayed argument is the ordinary inverse transform rotated through an angle proportional to the delay:

$$\Phi^{-1}\{F(\tau - \tau^*)\} = f(t)\exp(i\,\tau\,t^*). \qquad (4.21)$$

D. **Argument scaling:**

$$\Phi\{f(\alpha t)\} = (1/|\,\alpha\,|)\,F(\tau/\alpha). \qquad (4.22)$$

E. **Reflection in t = 0:** The transform of the function reflected in time about $t = 0$ is the reflection of the transform about $\tau = 0$:

$$\Phi\{f(-t)\} = F(-\tau). \qquad (4.23)$$

F. **The Transform of the transform:**

$$\Phi\{\Phi\{f(t)\}\} = 2\pi f(-t). \qquad (4.24)$$

4.2 PROPERTIES OF THE FOURIER TRANSFORM

DEFINITION 4.3: CONVOLUTION

Convolution is an operation which for a pair of functions produces a new function, the **convolution** of the first two. If $f(t)$ and $g(t)$ are absolutely integrable on the line $-\infty < t < \infty$ then their convolution, denoted by $f * g$, is the function $h(t)$ defined by

$$h(t) = (f * g)[t] = \int_{-\infty}^{\infty} f(t - \tau)\, g(\tau)\, d\tau. \qquad (4.25)$$

If we introduce a change of variables in the integral $s = t - \tau$ we find that the convolution operation is commutative,

$$f * g = g * f. \qquad (4.26)$$

EXAMPLE 4.2

Let

$$f(t) = 1 \text{ on } 0 \le t \le 1; = 0 \text{ elsewhere}$$

and

$$g(t) = 1 \text{ on } 2 \le t \le 3; = 0 \text{ elsewhere.}$$

Then their convolution $h = f * g$ is given by

$$h(t) = f * g[t] = \int_{-\infty}^{\infty} f(s) g(t - s) \, ds$$

But $f(s)$ vanishes everywhere outside of the unit interval, so that the integral is equal to its value over the interval [0,1] where $f \equiv 1$,

$$h(t) = \int_{0}^{1} g(t - s) \, ds.$$

Introducing the change of variable $u = t - s$ leads us to

$$h(t) = \int_{t-1}^{t} g(u) \, du$$

which defines the function (See Figure 4.1).

$$h(t) = \begin{cases} 0, & \text{for } t \le 2 \\ t - 2, & \text{for } 2 \le t \le 3 \\ 4 - t, & \text{for } 3 \le t \le 4 \\ 0, & \text{for } t \ge 4 \end{cases}$$

REMARK 4.2

One reason for the importance of the convolution is that it enables us to find the inverse Fourier transform of a product of

Fourier transforms. This is the content of the following theorem.

THEOREM 4.5: CONVOLUTION THEOREM

The Fourier transform of the convolution of two functions is equal to the product of their Fourier transforms:

$$\Phi(f * g) = \Phi\{f\}\Phi\{g\} \tag{4.27}$$

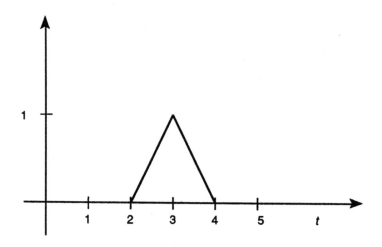

Figure 4.1– $Y = h(t)$

EXAMPLE 4.3

A straightforward calculation shows us that for f, g defined in Example 4.2,

$$\Phi\{f\}[s] = (i/s)[e^{-is} - 1]$$

(see Example 4.1), and

56

$$\Phi\{g\}[s] = (i/s)[e^{-3is} - e^{-2is}];$$

a more lengthy calculation shows that their product is indeed equal to the Fourier Transform of h(t) defined in Figure 4.1.

REMARK 4.3: THE FOURIER TRANSFORM AND THE FUNCTION

We have seen that the Fourier series expansion of $f(t)$ provides us with information about the decomposition of $f(t)$ into sinusoidal waves of various frequencies when $f(t)$ is periodic. In the same way the Fourier Transform tells us about the decomposition of $f(t)$ into sinusoidal waves even when f(t) is not periodic. Thus in the inverse formula

$$f(t) = (1/2\pi)\int_{-\infty}^{\infty} F(\tau)e^{i\tau t}d\tau \qquad (4.28)$$

regions on the line $-\infty < \tau < \infty$ in which the transform is greater in magnitude will effect $f(t)$ more strongly than others. In this way the Fourier Transform provides us with information about the function in a "frequency space" which is not available to us in the space of the independent variable of the function. The connection between the function and its transform is very strong, as is indicated by the following theorem presenting the Parseval identities for the Fourier Transform. We note that these identities are generalizations of the Parseval identity for the Fourier Series expansion.

THEOREM 4.6: PARSEVAL'S IDENTITIES

Let $f(t)$, $g(t)$ have Fourier transforms $F(\tau)$, $G(\tau)$, respectively. Then

$$\boxed{\int_{-\infty}^{\infty} f(t)g(t)\, dt = (1/2\pi)\int_{-\infty}^{\infty} F(\tau)\,\overline{G(\tau)}\, d\tau} \qquad (4.29)$$

where $G(\tau)$ is the complex conjugate of $G(\tau)$. Similarly,

$$\int_{-\infty}^{\infty} f(s)G(s)\,ds = \int_{-\infty}^{\infty} F(s)\,g(s)\,ds. \qquad \text{(4.29a)}$$

In the special case of $f = g$, the equation tells us

$$\int_{-\infty}^{\infty} f(t)^2\,dt = (1/2\pi)\int_{-\infty}^{\infty} |F(\tau)|^2\,d\tau. \qquad \text{(4.30)}$$

Thus the root-mean square norm of the function on the t-axis is in some sense preserved in value (modulo the factor 2π) in the space of definition of the Fourier Transform. Similarly

$$\int_{-\infty}^{\infty} f(s)G(s)\,ds = \int_{-\infty}^{\infty} F(s)\,g(s)\,ds. \qquad \text{(4.29a)}$$

We note that the Parseval identities carry over to the Fourier sine and cosine transforms.

THEOREM 4.7: CONTINUITY OF THE FOURIER TRANSFORM

If $f(t)$ is absolutely integrable on the t-axis then its Fourier transform $F(\tau)$ is continuous for all τ and tends to zero as $|\tau| \to \infty$.

REMARK 4.4

We have seen that the Fourier transform of the function that is equal to 1 on the unit interval and vanishes elsewhere is given by (Example 4.1):

$$F(\tau) = (i/\tau)[e^{-i\tau} - 1].$$

This function is continuous at $\tau = 0$ if we define it there, using L'Hospitals's rule, as 1. Clearly F tends to zero as $|\tau| \to \infty$ since

$$|F(\tau)| \le 2(1/|\tau|),$$

where we have used $|e^{-i\tau}| = 1$ for real τ.

THEOREM 4.8: DIFFERENTIATION AND THE FOURIER TRANSFORM

If

$$g(t) = t^n f(t)$$

is absolutely integrable for $n = 1, 2, \ldots$, then the Fourier transform $F(\tau)$ of $f(t)$ can be differentiated n times, with its kth derivative ($k \leq n$) given by

$$F^{(k)}(\tau) = (i^k/2\pi)(-1)^k \int_{-\infty}^{\infty} f(t)t^k e^{-itz}dt \qquad (4.31)$$

Every derivative converges to zero as $|\tau| \to \infty$.

THEOREM 4.9: THE TRANSFORM OF THE DERIVATIVE

The Fourier Transform of the derivative of a function $f(t)$ is given by

$$\Phi(f\,')[\tau] = \tau\, i\, \Phi(f). \qquad (4.32)$$

THEOREM 4.10: THE TRANSFORM OF THE INDEFINITE INTEGRAL

Let $g(t)$ be the indefinite integral of $f(t)$,

$$g(t) = \int_{0}^{t} f(s)\, ds. \qquad (4.33)$$

Then

$$\Phi(g)[\tau] = (1/i\,\tau)\Phi(f)[\tau]. \qquad (4.34)$$

DEFINITION 4.4: THE FOURIER TRANSFORM OF FUNCTIONS OF MORE THAN ONE VARIABLE

The Fourier Transform of the function $f(s, t)$ of two variables is

$$F(\sigma,\tau) = \int_{-\infty}^{\infty} \int_{-\infty}^{\infty} f(s,t)e^{-i(\sigma s + \tau t)}\,ds\,dt. \qquad (4.35)$$

The **inversion formula** for the transform is

$$f(s,t) = 1/(2\pi)^2 \int_{-\infty}^{\infty} \int_{-\infty}^{\infty} F(\sigma,\tau)e^{i(s\sigma + t\tau)}\,d\sigma\,d\tau \qquad (4.36)$$

4.3 SPECTRAL ANALYSIS

DEFINITION 4.5: MAGNITUDE SPECTRUM

The **magnitude spectrum** of the function $f(t)$ is the modulus of the Fourier Transform of f,

$$\text{MAGNITUDE SPECTRUM} = |F(\tau)|. \qquad (4.37)$$

DEFINITION 4.6: PHASE SPECTRUM

The **phase spectrum** of $f(t)$ is the argument of the Fourier Transform,

$$\text{PHASE SPECTRUM} = \arg(F(\tau)). \qquad (4.38)$$

EXAMPLE 4.4

For $f(t)$ equal to 1 on $(0, 1)$ and 0 elsewhere, we have seen that the Fourier Transform is

$$F(\tau) = (i/\tau)(e^{-i\tau} - 1).$$

Thus

$$F(\tau) = |F(\tau)|\, e^{i\,\arg(F(\tau))}$$

where by a straightforward calculation we find that

$$|F(\tau)| = (2/\tau) |\sin(\tau/2)|$$

and

$$\arg(F(\tau)) = -\tau/2.$$

CHAPTER 5

GENERALIZED FUNCTIONS

The Fourier Series frees us from the artificial need for infinite differentiability of functions imposed by the Taylor Series. Thus with minimization of error in the sense of the root-mean-square norm, the "best fitting" trigonometric polynomial can be found as long as the function to be approximated obeys the Dirichlet conditions.

While up to this point we have repeatedly demanded adherence to the Dirichlet conditions for the Fourier Series or absolute integrability for the Fourier Transform, we now free ourselves from even these limited restrictions, defining the concept of a "generalized" function. With this concept we can deal with functions that "jump" between values, that represent instantaneous "pulses" having power but no duration time, that do not converge to zero with larger arguments, etc. For all of these functions we develop a consistent definition of the Fourier Transform, of differentiability and integrability and of the use of the standard Calculus tools in this more general context.

DEFINITION 5.1: SMOOTH FUNCTIONS

A function $\phi(t)$ is **smooth** if it and its derivatives of all orders are defined and continuous for all t on $-\infty < t < \infty$.

EXAMPLE 5.1

The function

$$\phi(t) = \begin{cases} 0, & \text{for } t = 0 \\ \exp(-1/t^2), & \text{for } t \neq 0 \end{cases}$$

has derivatives of all orders for all values of t. Note that this function **cannot** be expanded in a Taylor series about $t = 0$ although there too, the function has continuous derivatives of all orders (with all derivatives equal to zero).

DEFINITION 5.2: COMPACT SUPPORT

A function $\phi(t)$ is said to have **compact support** if it vanishes outside of some finite interval,

$$\boxed{\phi(t) = 0 \text{ for } |t| > R, R = \text{sufficiently large.}}$$

DEFINITION 5.3: TEST FUNCTIONS

A **test function** is one which is smooth and has compact support.

REMARK 5.1: WHAT IS $\sqrt{2}$?

An irrational number such as $\sqrt{2}$ is defined as a **Cauchy sequence of rational numbers**. Such a sequence is defined by the decimals

$$x_1 = 1, \quad x_2 = 1.4, \quad x_3 = 1.414 \dots$$

The sequence is a **Cauchy sequence** since it obeys the condition

$$|x_m - x_n| \to 0 \text{ as } m, n \to \infty,$$

meaning that the rational numbers x_n are clustering ever closer to $\sqrt{2}$, although never reaching it except "in the limit." **What is $\sqrt{2}$?** It is the sequence of rationals that a) converge to it, and b) represent it to any desired level of accuracy.

DEFINITION 5.4:   GENERALIZED FUNCTIONS

A **generalized function** $f(t)$ is defined by a sequence $\{f_n(t)\}$ of test functions obeying the "Cauchy sequence" condition that for **any** test function $\phi(t)$,

$$\int_{-\infty}^{\infty} \phi(t) \{f_m(t) - f_n(t)\} \, dt \to 0 \qquad (5.1)$$

as $m, n \to \infty$. We say that $\{f_n\}$ converges to f in the weak sense or equivalently, f is the weak limit of $\{f_n\}$ if

$$\int_{-\infty}^{\infty} f_n(t) \phi(t) \, dt \to \int_{-\infty}^{\infty} f(t) \phi(t) \, dt \qquad (5.2)$$

for every test function ϕ.

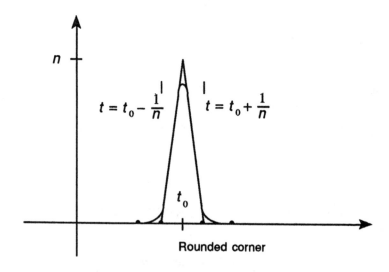

Figure 5.1–Approximating $\delta(t - t_0)$

64

EXAMPLE 5.2

Let t_0 be any point on the t-axis. For $n = 1, 2, \ldots$ let $f_n(t)$ be the function shown in Figure 5.1; f_n is obtained from the function

$$g_n(t) = \begin{cases} 0, & \text{for } t \leq (t_0 - 1/n) \\ n^2[t - t_0 + 1/n], & \text{for } t_0 - 1/n < t < t_0 \\ -n^2[t - t_0 - 1/n], & \text{for } t_0 < t < t_0 + 1/n \\ 0, & \text{for } t \geq (t_0 + 1/n) \end{cases}$$

by "rounding" the corners at $t_0 \pm 1/n$, t_0 with an infinitely differentiable "corner" as shown. Moreover, f_n will be chosen such that the area under its curve is equal to one for all n,

$$\int_{-\infty}^{\infty} f_n(t) \, dt = 1. \tag{5.3}$$

For any test function $\phi(t)$ the integral

$$\int_{-\infty}^{\infty} f_n(t) \, \phi(t) \, dt \tag{5.4}$$

is defined. Moreover, for n sufficiently large, the generalized mean value theorem of the calculus tells us that

$$\int_{-\infty}^{\infty} f_n(t) \, \phi(t) \, dt = \phi(t_n^*) \int_{-\infty}^{\infty} f_n(t) \, dt$$

$$= \phi(t_n^*) \tag{5.5}$$

The point t_n^* lies somewhere on the interval

$$t_0 - 1/n \leq t_n^* \leq t_0 + 1/n.$$

As $n \to \infty$ we see that

a) $t_n^* \to t_0$,

b)   the graph of f_n appears more and more like that of a verti-
      cal line of infinite height, with the proviso that the area
      under its graph is always equal to 1;

c)   from (5.5) the limit

$$\lim_{n \to \infty} \int_{-\infty}^{\infty} f_n(t) \, \phi(t) \, dt = \phi(t_0) .$$

The sequence of test functions $\{f_n\}$ converges weakly to a function, denoted by $\delta(t - t_0)$,

$$f_n(t) \to \delta(t - t_0)$$

and referred to as the "delta-function," satisfying the relation

$$\boxed{\int_{-\infty}^{\infty} \delta(t - t_0) \, \phi(t) \, dt = \phi(t_0) .} \qquad (5.6)$$

for all test functions $\phi(t)$.

DEFINITION 5.5:   THE DELTA FUNCTION

The delta function is the generalized function obeying (5.6)
for all test functions ϕ.

THEOREM 5.1:   PROPERTIES OF THE DELTA FUNCTION

$$\boxed{\text{(EVEN FUNCTION)} \qquad \delta(-t) = \delta(t)} \qquad (5.7)$$

$$\boxed{\delta(\alpha t) = (1/ |\alpha|) \, \delta(t)} \qquad (5.8)$$

$$f(t)\, \delta(t - t_0) = f(t_0)\, \delta(t - t_0) \qquad (5.9)$$

REMARK 5.2

The effect of the δ-function $\delta(t - t_0)$ is to "pluck out" the value of ϕ at t_0 in the inner product (5.6). The function is referred to as the "unit source" or "unit pulse" function because its integral is equal to 1. Note that the function **has no meaning** in the usual sense of attaining values at points t. Its only meaning is based on the relations (5.5, 6).

THEOREM 5.2

If for all test functions $\phi(t)$

$$\int_{-\infty}^{\infty} f(t)\, \phi(t)\, dt = \int_{-\infty}^{\infty} g(t)\, \phi(t)\, dt$$

then f and g are the same generalized function. If f and g happen to be continuous then they are identically equal.

DEFINITION 5.6:   GENERALIZED DERIVATIVE

Let $f(t)$ be a generalized function. The derivative $f'(t)$ of f is the generalized function satisfying the relation

$$\int_{-\infty}^{\infty} f'(t)\, \phi(t)\, dt = \int_{-\infty}^{\infty} f(t)\, \phi'(t)\, dt \qquad (5.10)$$

REMARK 5.3

If $f(t)$ is continuously differentiable then its derivative obeys (5.10). This is seen by applying integration by parts to the integral on the left side of (5.10).

THEOREM 5.3: GENERALIZED DERIVATIVE VERSUS CLASSICAL DERIVATIVE

If $f(t)$ is continuously differentiable everywhere then its classical derivative is equal to its generalized derivative.

DEFINITION 5.7: THE UNIT STEP FUNCTION

The **unit step function** is defined by

$$U(t) = \begin{cases} 0, & \text{for } t < 0 \\ {}^1\!/_2, & \text{for } t = 0 \\ 1, & \text{for } t > 0. \end{cases} \tag{5.11}$$

REMARK 5.4

Let $\phi(t)$ be any test function. Then the inner product of its derivative with the unit step function evaluated at a point $t - t_0$ for any t_0 is

$$\int_{-\infty}^{\infty} \phi'(t) U(t - t_0) \, dt = \int_{t_0}^{\infty} \phi'(t) \, dt$$

$$= -\phi(t_0)$$

But by the definition of the δ-function

$$\int_{-\infty}^{\infty} \delta(t - t_0) \phi(t) \, dt = \phi(t_0),$$

implying that for all test functions ϕ,

$$\int_{-\infty}^{\infty} \delta(t - t_0) \phi(t) \, dt = -\int_{-\infty}^{\infty} \phi'(t) U(t - t_0) \, dt,$$

that is, the δ-function is equal to the generalized derivative of the unit step function U.

DEFINITION 5.8: DERIVATIVES OF HIGHER ORDER

The nth derivative of the generalized function f, denoted by $f^{(n)}$, is defined by the relation

$$\int_{-\infty}^{\infty} f^{(n)}(t)\,\phi(t)\,dt = (-1)^n \int_{-\infty}^{\infty} f(t)\,\phi^{(n)}(t)\,dt \qquad (5.12)$$

for all test functions $\phi(t)$.

REMARK 5.5

Let $f(t)$ satisfy the Dirichlet conditions, having finitely many jumps at the points t_1, t_2, ..., t_N. At each point t_j denote the height of the jump by A_j,

$$A_j = f(t_j + 0) - f(t_j - 0).$$

Then $f(t)$ may be represented in the form

$$f(t) = g(t) + \sum_{j=1}^{N} A_j U(t - t_j)$$

where $g'(t)$ is piecewise continuous. The **generalized derivative of f(t)** is therefore

$$f'(t) = g'(t) + \sum_{j=1}^{N} A_j \delta(t - t_j).$$

CHAPTER 6

GENERALIZED FOURIER TRANSFORMS

The Fourier Transform was defined for absolutely integrable functions $f(t)$, obeying the condition

$$\int_{-\infty}^{\infty} |f(t)| \, dt < \infty. \tag{6.1}$$

This condition excludes such simple functions as constants and trigonometric functions. An approach to defining the Fourier Transform for such functions is indicated by our definition of generalized functions in terms of inner products with test functions. The **generalized Fourier transform** is defined by using this approach coupled with the Parseval equation.

6.1 BASIC CONCEPTS

DEFINITION 6.1: FUNCTIONS OF POLYNOMIAL GROWTH

A function $f(t)$ is of **polynomial growth** if for some natural number $N = 1, 2, \ldots,$ and all t sufficiently large

$$|f(t)| / |t|^N < M \tag{6.2}$$

for some bound M.

DEFINITION 6.2: FUNCTIONS OF POLYNOMIAL DECAY:

A function $f(t)$ is of **polynomial decay** if for some natural number $n = 1, 2, \ldots$, and all t sufficiently large

$$| f(t) | < M/| t |^N.$$ (6.3)

EXAMPLE 6.1

Some functions of polynomial growth are polynomials, trigonometric functions, and piecewise constant functions such as the unit step function $U(t)$.

EXAMPLE 6.2

Functions of polynomial decay include the negative exponential function $e^{-|t|}$, test functions of compact support and reciprocals of polynomials of the form $1/P(t)$ for polynomials P.

DEFINITION 6.3: GENERALIZED FUNCTIONS

A generalized function f of polynomial growth is one for which the inner product

$$(f, \phi) = \int_{-\infty}^{\infty} f(t)\ \phi(t)\ dt$$ (6.4)

can be defined for all test functions of polynomial decay, and obeys the **linearity condition**

$$(f, (\alpha_1\ \phi_1 + \alpha_2\ \phi_2)) = \alpha_1(f,\ \phi) + \alpha_2(f,\ \phi).$$ (6.5)

REMARK 6.1

If a function $f(t)$ has polynomial decay then for some M, if $t > M$, there are natural numbers A, N for which

$$|f(t)| < A/t^N$$

But then

$$\int_M^\infty |f(t)|\,dt < A \int_M^\infty t^{-N}\,dt = A/[M^{N-1}(N-1)].$$

The same inequality will apply to the interval extending to $-\infty$, while the integral on $[-M, M]$ is of course finite. Therefore $f(t)$ is absolutely integrable on the entire t axis, and we have:

THEOREM 6.1: POLYNOMIAL DECAY IMPLIES ABSOLUTELY INTEGRABLE

If $f(t)$ has polynomial decay then it is absolutely integrable.

REMARK 6.2

Since an absolutely integrable function has a Fourier Transform we conclude the following:

THEOREM 6.2: A FUNCTION HAVING POLYNOMIAL DECAY HAS A FOURIER TRANSFORM

We recall Parseval's Theorem on the inner product of a function with the Fourier Transform of a second function.

THEOREM 6.3

Let f, g be functions having the Fourier Transforms F, G, respectively. Then (Theorem 4.6),

$$\int_{-\infty}^{\infty} F(s)\,g(s)\,ds = \int_{-\infty}^{\infty} f(s)\,G(s)\,ds. \qquad (6.6)$$

DEFINITION 6.4: THE GENERALIZED FOURIER TRANSFORM

Let f be a function of polynomial growth, and let ϕ be any function of polynomial decay having the Fourier Transform G. Then the Fourier Transform F of f

$$F = \Phi\{f\}$$

is the generalized function which we define by the Parseval Identity (6.6),

$$(F, \phi) = (f, G)$$

or

$$\int_{-\infty}^{\infty} F(s)\,\phi(s)\,ds = \int_{-\infty}^{\infty} f(s)\,G(s)\,ds. \qquad (6.7)$$

EXAMPLE 6.3

The generalized Fourier Transforms of some common functions are:

a) $f(t) \equiv 1, \quad \Phi(f)[s] = 2\pi\delta(s)$

b) $f(t) = \delta(t), \quad \Phi(f)[s] \equiv 1$

c) $f(t) = e^{i\omega_0 t}, \quad \Phi(f)[s] = 2\pi\delta(s - \omega_0)$

d) $f(t) = U(t) = $ unit step function, $\Phi(f)[s] = \pi\delta(s) + 1/(is)$

e) $f(t) = \cos(\omega_0 t), \quad \Phi(f)[s] = \pi[\delta(s - \omega_0) + \delta(s + \omega_0)]$

DEFINITION 6.5: ENERGY CONTENT OF A FUNCTION

The **energy content** of a function $f(t)$ is the square of the norm

$$\text{ENERGY CONTENT} = \int_{-\infty}^{\infty} |f(t)|^2 \, dt \qquad (6.8)$$

REMARK 6.3

By Parseval's Theorem (4.6) the energy content of a function $f(t)$ with Fourier Transform $F(\tau)$ is

$$\text{ENERGY CONTENT} = \int_{-\infty}^{\infty} |f(t)|^2 \, dt$$

$$= (1/2\pi) \int_{-\infty}^{\infty} |F(\tau)|^2 \, d\tau \qquad (6.9)$$

so that the energy content of f is equal to the area under the curve of the square of the Fourier Transform (with the factor $1/2\pi$). Accordingly we define:

DEFINITION 6.6: ENERGY SPECTRUM

The function

$$S(\tau) = |F(\tau)|^2 \qquad (6.10)$$

is the **energy spectrum** or **energy spectral density** of $f(t)$.

6.2 CORRELATION

DEFINITION 6.7: CORRELATION

The function

$$R_{12}(\tau) = \int_{-\infty}^{\infty} f_1(t) f_2(t - \tau) \, dt \qquad (6.11)$$

is the **cross-correlation function** of f_1 and f_2.

The importance of the cross-correlation function is indicated in the following example:

EXAMPLE 6.4

Let the functions f_1, f_2 be defined as

$$f_1(t) = 1, \text{ on } 0 < t < 1; \ = 0 \text{ elsewhere}$$

$$f_2(t) = 1, \text{ on } 1 < t < 2; \ = 0 \text{ elsewhere.}$$

Substitution into (6.11) shows that

$$R_{12}(\tau) = \begin{cases} 0, & \text{for } t \leq -2 \\ t + 2, & \text{for } -2 < t < -1 \\ -t, & \text{for } -1 \leq t < 0 \\ 0, & \text{for } t \geq 0 \end{cases} \quad (6.12)$$

(see Figure 6.1). This means that if we shift f_2 to the left by τ then for $\tau = -1$ the overlap between the functions is greatest, as it obviously is; a shift of more than 2 to the left, or a shift to the right to any extent results in no overlap between the functions at all. Generally speaking the **cross-correlation** is a measure of similarity of the two functions.

REMARK 6.4

The cross-correlation is a measure of the similarity of information transmitted by two signals which are possibly displaced in time or in space. The effect of τ is to measure the similarity of the signals that one would observe by shifting them through a value τ.

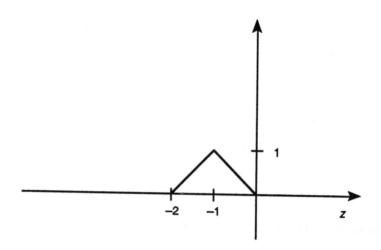

Figure 6.1– $R_{12}(z)$

DEFINITION 6.8:   UNCORRELATED FUNCTIONS

Two functions f_1, f_2 are **uncorrelated** if their cross-correlation function $R_{12}(\tau)$ is zero for all values of τ.

DEFINITION 6.9:   AUTO-CORRELATION

The **auto-correlation** function of $f(t)$ is

$$R_{11}(\tau) = \int_{-\infty}^{\infty} f(t) f(t - \tau) \, dt \qquad (6.13)$$

DEFINITION 6.9A: AUTO-CORRELATION-Alternate Definition

The auto-correlation of $f(t)$ is sometimes represented by

$$R_{11}(\tau) = (1/\|f\|^2) \int_{-\infty}^{\infty} f(t) f(t - \tau) \, dt \qquad (6.14)$$

for

$$\| f \|^2 = \text{ENERGY CONTENT OF } f.$$

THEOREM 6.4: FOURIER TRANSFORMS OF CORRELATIONS

Let $F_1(\tau)$, $F_2(\tau)$ be the Fourier Transforms of f_1, f_2, respectively, Then the Fourier Transforms of the cross-correlation and auto-correlation functions of f_1 and f_2 are given by

$$\Phi\{R_{12}\}[s] = F_1(s)F_2(-s) \qquad (6.15)$$

$$\Phi\{R_{11}\}[s] = F_1(s)F_1(-s) \qquad (6.16)$$

THEOREM 6.5: WIENER-KHINTCHINE THEOREM

The auto-correlation function R_{11} and the energy spectral density F for a given function f are a Fourier Transform pair:

$$| F(\tau) |^2 = \Phi\{R_{11}\}[\tau] . \qquad (6.17)$$

$$R_{11} = \Phi^{-1}\{ | F(\tau) |^2 \} \qquad (6.18)$$

77

CHAPTER 7

SPECIAL FUNCTIONS

Using the results of Chapter 3 we know how to represent a given function $f(t)$ in a Fourier Series expansion with respect to any orthonormal family of functions $\{\phi_n(t)\}$:

$$f(t) = \sum_{n=1}^{\infty} \alpha_n \, \phi_n(t); \qquad (7.1)$$

here the Fourier coefficients α_n are given by the inner products

$$\alpha_n = (f, \phi_n). \qquad (7.2)$$

If orthonormality of the $\{\phi_n\}$ is not assumed then (7.2) becomes

$$\alpha_n = (f, \phi_n) / \| \phi_n \|^2. \qquad (7.3)$$

The choice of the collection or **basis** of functions $\{\phi_n\}$ depends on the problem of interest to us. If it is a Sturm-Liouville problem (Definition 3.19) then the $\{\phi_n\}$ can be chosen to be the eigenfunctions of the equation. On the other hand, if the problem has some underlying periodicity then the trigonometric functions may serve as an appropriate basis.

This chapter reviews some function families having properties that in certain cases make them ideal candidates for basis functions. In each case the functions are eigenfunctions of a Sturm-Liouville problem for a second order ordinary differential equation. For each we will present the equation, the orthogonality relation, the form of the Fourier Series expansion, and some basic properties of the functions.

7.1 GAMMA AND BESSEL FUNCTIONS

DEFINITION 7.1: GAMMA FUNCTIONS

For $p > 0$ the Gamma function is defined as

$$\Gamma(p) = \int_0^\infty e^{-t} t^{p-1} \, dt. \qquad (7.4)$$

THEOREM 7.1: THE GAMMA FUNCTION FOR p = 1, 2, ...

For p, a natural number, $p = 1, 2, \ldots$,

$$\Gamma(p + 1) = p! \qquad (7.5)$$

DEFINITION 7.2: BESSEL'S EQUATION

Bessel's equation is the second order differential equation

$$t^2 y'' + t y' + (t^2 - m^2) y = 0 \qquad (7.6)$$

where m is a constant.

From the theory of linear second order differential equations we know that any solution can be written as the linear combination of any two linearly independent solutions,

$$y(t) = a_1 y_1(t) + a_2 y_2(t)$$

for appropriate constants a_1, a_2.

THEOREM 7.2 BESSEL FUNCTIONS

For any m Bessel's equation has a solution $J_m(t)$ having a finite limit as $t \rightarrow 0$, and a solution $Y_m(t)$ which is unbounded as $t \rightarrow 0$. J_m is called a Bessel function of the first kind of order m; Y_m is called a Bessel function of the second kind of order m or a **Neumann function**.

REMARK 7.1

The Bessel functions of first and second kind can be found by the **Frobenius method**, in which we seek a solution in the form

$$y = \sum_{n=-\infty}^{\infty} a_n t^{n+\beta}. \tag{7.7}$$

THEOREM 7.3: SERIES REPRESENTATION OF THE BESSEL FUNCTIONS OF THE FIRST KIND

The Bessel function of the first kind can be expanded in the form

$$J_m(t) = \sum_{n=0}^{\infty} \{(-1)^n (t/2)^{m+2n}\}$$

$$/\{\Gamma(n+1)\Gamma(m+n+1)\} \tag{7.8}$$

For m, a natural number, $m = 1, 2, \ldots,$ (7.5) implies

$$J_m(t) = \sum_{n=0}^{\infty} \{(-1)^n (t/2)^{2n+m}\}/\{n!(m+n)!\} \tag{7.9}$$

DEFINITION 7.3: J_m FOR NEGATIVE m

The Bessel Function of order m for $m < 0$ is defined by replacing m by $-m$ in (7.8).

THEOREM 7.4: RELATION BETWEEN J_m AND J_{-m} FOR INTEGER m

For $m = \pm 1, \pm 2, \ldots,$

$$J_{-m}(t) = (-1)^m J_m(t). \tag{7.10}$$

THEOREM 7.5: THE CASE OF NON-INTEGER m

If m is not an integer then J_m and J_{-m} are linearly independent; in this case the general solution of Bessel's equation is

$$y = a_1 J_m + a_2 J_{-m}. \tag{7.11}$$

THEOREM 7.6: THE GENERAL SOLUTION FOR INTEGER m:

For integer m (7.10) implies that J_m and J_{-m} are linearly dependent. In this case J_m together with the Neumann function Y_m define a linearly independent pair of solutions to Bessel's equation, for which every solution can be represented in the form

$$y = a_1 J_m + a_2 Y_m. \tag{7.12}$$

THEOREM 7.7: SERIES REPRESENTATION OF THE NEUMANN FUNCTION

For integer m the Neumann function is given by the series

$$Y_m(t) = (2/\pi)[ln(t/2) + \gamma]J_m(t)$$

$$- (1/\pi)\sum_{k=0}^{m-1} (m-k-1)!(t/2)^{2k-m}/k! \tag{7.13}$$

$$- (1/\pi)\sum_{k=0}^{\infty} (-1)^k \{W(k)+W(m+k)\}(t/2)^{2k+m}/[k!(m+k)!]$$

where

$$\gamma = 0.5772156\dots$$

is **Euler's constant** and W is the function

$$W(k) = 1 + 1/2 + 1/3 + \dots + 1/k.$$

DEFINITION 7.4: HANKEL FUNCTIONS

The Bessel functions of the third kind or **Hankel functions**, $H_m^{(1)}$ and $H_m^{(2)}$, are defined as

$$H_m^{(1)} = J_m + i\,Y_m \tag{7.14}$$

and

$$H_m^{(2)} = J_m - i\,Y_m. \tag{7.15}$$

THEOREM 7.8: GENERATING FUNCTION FOR J_m

The Bessel functions of the first kind $J_m(t)$ can be obtained from the **generation function** $\exp[\tfrac{1}{2}t(s - 1/s)]$ through the expansion relation

$$\exp[\tfrac{1}{2}t(s - 1/s)] = \sum_{m=-\infty}^{\infty} J_m(t)s^m. \tag{7.16}$$

THEOREM 7.9: RECURRENCE RELATIONS FOR THE BESSEL FUNCTIONS

If C_m represents any of the functions J_m, Y_m or $H_m^{(1)}$, $H_m^{(2)}$, then each of the following holds:

$$C_{m+1}(t) = (2m/t)\,C_m(t) - C_{m-1}(t) \tag{7.17}$$

$$C_m' = \tfrac{1}{2}[C_{m-1} - C_{m+1}] \tag{7.18}$$

$$tC_m'(t) = mC_m(t) - tC_{m+1}(t) \tag{7.19}$$

$$tC_m'(t) = tC_{m-1}(t) - mC_m(t) \tag{7.20}$$

$$(d/dt)[t^m C_m(t)] = t^m C_{m-1}(t) \tag{7.21}$$

$$(d/dt)[t^{-m} C_m(t)] = -t^{-m} C_{m+1}(t) \tag{7.22}$$

THEOREM 7.10: BEHAVIOR FOR t ≈ 0

For $t \approx 0$

$$J_m(t) \approx (\tfrac{1}{2}t)^m/m! \tag{7.23}$$

$$Y_0(t) \approx (2/\pi)\ln(t) \tag{7.24}$$

$$Y_m(t) \approx -(1/\pi)(m-1)!(2/t)^m. \tag{7.25}$$

THEOREM 7.11: BEHAVIOR FOR t → ∞

For $t \to \infty$,

$$J_m(t) \approx (2/\pi t)^{1/2} \cos\{t - \tfrac{1}{2}m\pi - \tfrac{1}{4}\pi\} \tag{7.26}$$

$$Y_m(t) \approx (2/\pi t)^{1/2} \sin\{t - \tfrac{1}{2}m\pi - \tfrac{1}{4}\pi\} \tag{7.27}$$

$$H_m^{(1)}(t) \approx (2/\pi t)^{1/2} \exp\{i(t - \tfrac{1}{2}m\pi - \tfrac{1}{4})\} \tag{7.28}$$

$$H_m^{(2)}(t) \approx (2/\pi t)^{1/2} \exp\{-i(t - \tfrac{1}{2}m\pi - \tfrac{1}{4})\} \tag{7.29}$$

THEOREM 7.12: RELATION BETWEEN $J_{1/2}$ AND sin

The Bessel functions of first kind for $m = 1/2, 3/2, \ldots$, can be written in terms of the trigonometric functions. For example,

$$J_{1/2}(t) = (2/\pi t)^{1/2} \sin(t). \qquad (7.30)$$

REMARK 7.2: A WEIGHTED INNER PRODUCT

For our purposes, in working with the Bessel functions, we will now define the **weighted inner product** of functions

$$(f,g)_\omega = \int_0^1 t f(t)\, g(t)\, dt \qquad (7.31)$$

With this inner product all the results of Chapter 3 remain correct. In particular the **norm** of a function f is given by

$$\|f\|^2 = \int_0^1 t f(t)^2\, dt \qquad (7.32)$$

THEOREM 7.13: AN INNER PRODUCT RELATION FOR THE BESSEL FUNCTIONS

For any α, β,

$$\int_0^1 t J_m(\alpha t) J_m(\beta t)\, dt$$

$$= \{ \alpha J_m(\beta) J_{m}{'}(\alpha) - \beta J_m(\alpha) J_{m}{'}(\beta) \} / \{ \beta^2 - \alpha^2 \}. \qquad (7.33)$$

THEOREM 7.14: ORTHOGONALITY RELATIONS FOR THE BESSEL FUNCTIONS

If either or both of the values α, β are zeros of the Bessel function J_m, then the functions

$$\boxed{f(t) = J_m(\alpha t), \; g(t) = J_m(\beta t)} \qquad (7.34)$$

are orthogonal in the sense of the weighted inner product,

$$\boxed{(f,g)_\omega = \int_0^1 tf(t)\, g(t)\, dt.} \qquad (7.35)$$

THEOREM 7.15: NORM OF THE BESSEL FUNCTION

If α is a zero of $J_m(\alpha)$ then the norm $||f||$ of the function

$$f(t) = J_m(\alpha t)$$

is given by

$$||f||^2 = \int_0^1 tf(t)^2\, dt$$

$$= \frac{1}{2} J_m{}'(\alpha)^2$$

THEOREM 7.16: THE ZEROES OF $J_m(t)$

The Bessel function has a sequence of positive zeroes which may be arranged in increasing order $\alpha_1, a_2, \ldots$.

Thus the first four zeroes of J_2 are, to two decimal places, 5.14, 8.42, 11.62 and 14.80.

THEOREM 7.17: THE FOURIER-BESSEL SERIES

Let $f(t)$ be a piecewise continuous function with piecewise continuous derivative on $0 \le t \le 1$. Then $f(t)$ may be expanded in a **Fourier-Bessel** Series in the orthogonal family of Bessel functions

$$\boxed{f_n(t) = J_m(\alpha_n t)} \qquad (7.36)$$

85

where $\{\alpha_n\}$ is the sequence of positive zeroes of the Bessel function and $m \geq -\frac{1}{2}$. The series takes the form

$$f(t) = \sum_{n=1}^{\infty} c_j f_n(t) \tag{7.37}$$

where for $j = 1, 2, \dots$,

$$c_j = (f, f_j)\omega / \|f_j\|^2 \tag{7.38}$$

with uniform convergence taking place in any closed interval of continuity of f.

REMARK 7.3:

We note that Bessel's inequality (3.20) and Parseval's identity (3.24) remain valid for the Fourier-Bessel series.

7.2   LEGENDRE POLYNOMIALS

DEFINITION 7.5:   LEGENDRE'S DIFFERENTIAL EQUATION

Legendre's differential equation is

$$(1 - t^2)y'' - 2ty' + m(m + 1)y = 0. \tag{7.39}$$

THEOREM 7.18: LEGENDRE POLYNOMIALS

Consider the equation (7.39) on the interval $-1 \leq t \leq 1$. An orthogonal family of solutions in the sense of the inner product

$$(f, g) = \int_{-1}^{1} f(t)\, g(t)\, dt$$

is the collection of **Legendre Polynomials** $P_n(t)$, the first four of which are

$$P_0(t) \equiv 1, \quad P_1(t) = t$$

$$P_2(t) = \tfrac{1}{2}(3t^2 - 1), \quad P_3(t) = \tfrac{1}{2}(5t^3 - 3t)$$

The Legendre polynomials obey the relations

$$\int_{-1}^{1} P_m(t)P_n(t)\,dt = \begin{cases} 0, & \text{for } m \neq n \\ 2/(2n+1), & \text{for } m = n \end{cases} \quad (7.40)$$

THEOREM 7.19: RODRIGUE'S FORMULA

The Legendre polynomials are given by the **Rodrigue's formula**

$$P_m(t) = [1/(2^m m!)]d^m/dt^m\{(t^2 - 1)^m\}. \quad (7.41)$$

THEOREM 7.20: GENERATING FUNCTION FOR LEGENDRE POLYNOMIALS

The **generating function** for the Legendre polynomials is given by

$$1/\{1 - 2st + t^2\}^{1/2} = \sum_{m=0}^{\infty} P_m(s)t^m \quad (7.42)$$

THEOREM 7.21: RECURRENCE FORMULAS FOR LEGENDRE POLYNOMIALS

$$P_{m+1}(t) = [(2m+1)/(m+1)]tP_m(t) - [m/(m+1)]P_{m-1}(t) \quad (7.43)$$

$$P_{m+1}(t) = 2(m+1)P_m(t) + P_{m-1}(t) \quad (7.44)$$

THEOREM 7.22: LEGENDRE-FOURIER SERIES EXPANSION

Let $f(t)$ and $f'(t)$ be piecewise continuous on the interval

87

$$-1 < t < 1.$$

Then $f(t)$ may be represented by a Legendre-Fourier series of the form

$$f(t) = \sum_{m=0}^{\infty} \alpha_m P_m(t) \qquad (7.45)$$

where the **Legendre-Fourier coefficients** α_m are given by

$$\alpha_m = (f, P_m) / \| P_m \|^2 \qquad (7.46)$$

with

$$\| P_m \|^2 = 2/(2m + 1). \qquad (7.47)$$

7.3   SOME ADDITIONAL SPECIAL FUNCTIONS

Some additional special functions arising in various applications are the **Hermite** and **Laguerre polynomials.** We will now list the differential equation giving rise to each of these function families, together with the orthogonality and recurrence relations for each case.

DEFINITION 7.6:   HERMITE DIFFERENTIAL EQUATION AND POLYNOMIALS

The **Hermite polynomial** of order m denoted by $H_m(t)$ is a solution to the Hermite differential equation

$$y'' - 2ty' + 2my = 0, \, m = 0, 1, 2, \dots . \qquad (7.48)$$

REMARK 7.4

The first four Hermite polynomials are

$$H_0(t) \equiv 1, \quad H_1(t) = 2t$$

$$H_2(t) = 4t^2 - 2, \quad H_3(t) = 8t^3 - 12\,t$$

THEOREM 7.23: RECURRENCE RELATIONS

$$H_{m+1}(t) = 2tH_m(t) - 2mH_{m-1}(t) \qquad (7.49)$$

$$H_m'(t) = 2mH_{m-1}(t) \qquad (7.50)$$

DEFINITION 7.7: A WEIGHTED INNER PRODUCT FOR THE HERMITE POLYNOMIALS

Define the Hermite-weighted inner product as

$$(f,g)_{\omega^h} = \int_{-\infty}^{\infty} \exp(-t^2) f(t)\, g(t)\, dt \qquad (7.51)$$

and the norm as

$$(\|f\|_{\omega}^{h})^2 = (f,f)_{\omega}^{h} \qquad (7.52)$$

THEOREM 7.24: ORTHGONALITY OF THE HERMITE POLYNOMIALS

The Hermite polynomials obey the orthogonality relations

$$(H_m, H_n)_{\omega}^{h} = \begin{cases} 0, & \text{for } m \neq n \\ 2^n n! \sqrt{\pi}, & m = n. \end{cases} \qquad (7.53)$$

DEFINITION 7.8: LAGUERRE DIFFERENTIAL EQUATION AND POLYNOMIALS

The Laguerre polynomial of order m denoted by $L_m(t)$ is a solution to the Laguerre differential equation

$$ty'' + (1-t)y' + my = 0, m = 0, 1, 2, \ldots \qquad (7.54)$$

REMARK 7.5

The first four Laguerre polynomials are

$$L_0(t) = 1, \qquad L_1(t) = 1 - t$$

$$L_2(t) = t^2 - 4t + 2 \qquad L_3(t) = 6 - 18t + 9t^2 - t^3$$

THEOREM 7.25: RECURRENCE RELATIONS

$$L_{m+1}(t) = (2m + 1 - t) L_m(t) - m^2 L_{m-1}(t) \qquad (7.55)$$

$$L_m'(t) = mL_{m-1}'(t) - mL_{m-1}(t) \qquad (7.56)$$

DEFINITION 7.9: A WEIGHTED INNER PRODUCT FOR THE LAGUERRE POLYNOMIALS

Define the Laguerre-weighted inner product as

$$(f,g)_\omega^L = \int_0^\infty e^{-t} f(t) g(t) dt \qquad (7.57)$$

and the norm as

$$(\|f\|_\omega^L)^2 = \int_0^\infty e^{-t} f(t)^2 dt. \qquad (7.58)$$

THEOREM 7.26: ORTHOGONALITY OF THE LAGUERRE POLYNOMIALS

The Laguerre polynomials obey the orthogonality relations

$$
(L_m, L_n)_\omega^L = \begin{cases} 0, & \text{for } m \neq n \\ (n!)^2, & \text{for } m = n. \end{cases} \tag{7.59}
$$

CHAPTER 8

APPLICATIONS

Fourier Analysis techniques are applied in many fields. In this chapter we see examples of these applications in the solution of three basic problems in partial differential equations.

8.1 FOURIER SERIES FOR SOLVING THE HEAT EQUATION

Consider a one-dimensional slab $0 \leq x \leq L$ bounded by faces at $x = 0$ and $x = L$. At each of these faces the temperature is fixed at a constant value which we assume to be zero. At some initial time we know the temperature distribution throughout the slab. In addition the thermophysical properties of the slab are known to us. We wish to find the temperature distribution in the slab as a function of time for later times.

We will denote by $T(x, t)$ the temperature at the point x at the time t. The "initial time" corresponds to the value $t = 0$. The **boundary conditions** of our problem are expressed mathematically as

$$T(0, t) = t(\text{L}, t) \equiv 0, \text{ for } t > 0. \tag{8.1}$$

The "initial condition," according to which the temperature distribution at some initial time is known, may be represented mathematically by the relation

$$T(x, 0) = f(x), \ 0 \le x \le L, \qquad (8.2)$$

where $f(x)$ is a known function.

We assume that the heat transfer characteristics of the material comprising the slab are fully represented by a thermophysical constant, the **thermal diffusivity**, denoted by α.

Conduction heat transfer in the slab is represented by the assumption that the temperature $T(x, t)$ obeys the **heat equation**, the partial differential equation

$$T_t(x, t) = \alpha T_{xx}(x, t), \ 0 \le x \le L, \ t > 0. \qquad (8.3)$$

Here T_t and T_{xx} represent, respectively, the first partial derivative with respect to t and the second partial derivative with respect to x.

The problem of finding the temperature history in the slab can now be represented mathematically as follows:

PROBLEM 1

Find a function $T(x, t)$ for $0 \le x \le L$, $t > 0$, obeying the heat equation (8.3), the initial condition (8.2) and the boundary conditions (8.1) [Figure 8.1].

A formula for the solution to this problem can be derived by combining the method of **separation of variables** and the Fourier series expansion for the initial temperature $f(x)$.

If we assume that f, together with its first derivative f', are piecewise continuous on $0 \le x \le L$, then we may extend f to the

93

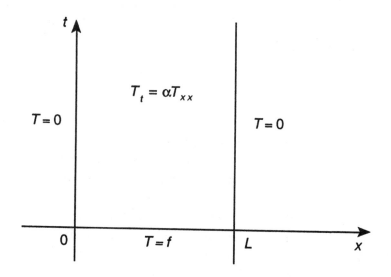

Figure 8.1–A Heat Conduction Problem

entire interval $-L \leq x \leq L$ as an odd function, admitting a sine-Fourier series expansion

$$f(x) = \sum_{n=1}^{\infty} a_n \sin(n\pi x/L) \tag{8.4}$$

with the Fourier coefficients

$$a_n = (2/L) \int_0^L f(s) \sin(n\pi s/L) \, ds. \tag{8.5}$$

For any n let

$$g(x, t) = \exp(-(\pi n/L)^2 \alpha t) \sin(\pi n x/L); \tag{8.6}$$

g is a **separable** solution to the heat equation (8.3) of the form

$$g(x, t) = X(x) Y(t). \tag{8.7}$$

Moreover g satisfies the boundary conditions (8.1) since the

94

sine function vanishes at $x = 0, L$. If we now form the series

$$T(x,t) = \sum_{n=1}^{\infty} \exp(-(\pi n/L)^2 \alpha t) \sin(\pi nx/L) \quad (8.8)$$

then we may show that $T(x, t)$, as the sum of solutions g over all n, satisfies the heat equation (8.3), the boundary conditions (8.1) (since the functions g all vanish at $x = 0, L$) and the initial condition (8.2) (since the a_n are the Fourier coefficients of f). Therefore (8.8) is the solution to Problem 1.

8.2 FOURIER TRANSFORM IN SOLVING THE HEAT EQUATION

In our next case we will use the Fourier Transform to solve a heat conduction problem. Our problem this time is determining the time history of the temperature on the entire infinite slab $-\infty < x < \infty$, subject to the condition that at some initial time the temperature distribution on the line was prescribed by a given, absolutely integrable function. Thus, our problem differs from Problem 1 in the sense that the interval of the slab is now the entire line, so that we do not have boundary conditions prescribed, while the initial condition (8.2) now becomes

$$T(x, 0) = f(x), -\infty < x < \infty . \quad (8.9)$$

PROBLEM 2

Find the function $T(x, t)$ satisfying the heat equation (8.3) for $-\infty < x < \infty, t > 0$, subject to the initial condition (8.2).

To solve this problem we make use of the following result:

$$\int_{-\infty}^{\infty} \exp(-x^2)\, dx = \sqrt{\pi}. \quad (8.10)$$

For any value of s the function

$$g(x, t) = \exp\{- isx - \alpha s^2 t\}$$ (8.11)

satisfies the heat equation. Thus, we may seek the solution to Problem 2 in the form

$$T(x,t) = \int_{-\infty}^{\infty} \phi(s) \exp\{- isx - \alpha s^2 t\} \, ds.$$ (8.12)

For $t = 0$ the initial condition (8.9) would then imply

$$f(x) = \int_{-\infty}^{\infty} \phi(s) \exp(- isx) \, ds$$ (8.13)

which simply states that f is the Fourier Transform of ϕ. But then by the Fourier Transform inversion relation,

$$\phi(s) = (1/2\pi) \int_{-\infty}^{\infty} f(u) \exp(ius) \, du.$$ (8.14)

Substituting this into (8.12), interchanging the order of integration and using (8.10) results in

$$T(x,t) = [1/2\sqrt{\pi} \, \alpha t] \int_{-\infty}^{\infty} f(s) \exp[- (x - s)^2 / 4\alpha t] \, ds$$ (8.15)

which is the formula for the solution to Problem 2.

8.3 BESSEL FUNCTIONS AND HEAT TRANSFER IN A CYLINDER

Many heat transfer problems arise in connection with cylindrically shaped bodies. For this geometry the natural choice of separable solutions to the equation is based on the use of Bessel functions. To see this, consider the problem of heat transfer in a cylinder of radius $r = a$, subject to the boundary condition of zero temperature on the cylinder wall and an initial known temperature distribution which is dependent only on the radial distance from the cylinder axis. The temperature is then given by a function $T(r, t)$ dependent only on time t and radial distance r from the axis, and our problem takes the following form:

PROBLEM 3

Find the function $T(r, t)$, $0 \le r \le a$, $t > 0$, satisfying the **heat equation** in **cylindrical coordinates**

$$T_t(r, t) = (\alpha/r)(rT_r)_r \qquad (8.16)$$

together with the initial condition

$$T(r, 0) = f(r), \, 0 \le r \le a \qquad (8.17)$$

and the boundary condition

$$T(a, t) \equiv 0, \, t > 0. \qquad (8.18)$$

We begin the solution by separating variables and noting that the function

$$g(r, t) = J_0(\beta r) \exp(-\alpha\beta^2 t) \qquad (8.19)$$

satisfies the equation (8.16) and the boundary condition (8.18) if β is any root of the equation

$$J_0(\beta a) = 0. \qquad (8.20)$$

But there are infinitely many real, positive roots of this equation, constituting a sequence $\{\beta_n\}$. Furthermore in the sense of the weighted inner product (7.35),

$$(f, g)_\omega = \int_0^1 t f(t) \, g(t) \, dt,$$

the functions $J_0(\beta_n r)$ are mutually orthogonal. Therefore we can expand the function $f(r)$ in a Fourier-Bessel Series

$$f(r) = \sum_{n=1}^{\infty} a_n J_0(\beta_n r),$$ (8.21)

where the a_n are the Fourier coefficients given by (7.38). Thus the solution to Problem 3 is given by the series

$$T(r,t) = \sum_{n=1}^{\infty} a_n J_0(\beta_n r) \exp(-\alpha \beta_n^2 t).$$ (8.22)

HANDBOOK AND GUIDE FOR
COMPARING and SELECTING
COMPUTER LANGUAGES

BASIC	PL/1
FORTRAN	APL
PASCAL	ALGOL-60
COBOL	C

- **This book is the first of its kind ever produced in computer science.**

- **It examines and highlights the differences and similarities among the eight most widely used computer languages.**

- **A practical guide for selecting the most appropriate programming language for any given task.**

- **Sample programs in all eight languages are written and compared side-by-side. Their merits are analyzed and evaluated.**

- **Comprehensive glossary of computer terms.**

Available at your local bookstore or order directly from us by sending in coupon below.

RESEARCH and EDUCATION ASSOCIATION
61 Ethel Road W., Piscataway, New Jersey 08854
Phone: (201) 819-8880

VISA   MasterCard

Charge Card Number

Please check one box:

☐ Payment enclosed

☐ Visa
☐ Master Card

Expiration Date _____ / _____
                    Mo   Yr

Please ship the "Computer Languages Handbook" @ $8.95 plus $2.00 for shipping.

Name _____

Address _____

City _____ State _____ Zip_____

HANDBOOK AND GUIDE
FOR
SELECTING A CAREER
AND PREPARING FOR THE FUTURE

For:

- **Young Job-Seekers**
- **Persons Seeking a Career Change**
- **Persons Entering the Labor Force Later In Life**

Over 250 careers are covered. Each career is described in detail including:

- **Training and Education**
- **Character of the Work Performed**
- **Working Conditions**
- **Amount of Earnings**
- **Advancement Opportunities**

Available at your local bookstore or order directly from us by sending in coupon below.

RESEARCH and EDUCATION ASSOCIATION
61 Ethel Road W., Piscataway, New Jersey 08854
Phone: (201) 819-8880

VISA   **MasterCard**

Please check one box:

☐ Payment enclosed

☐ Visa
☐ Master Card

Charge Card Number

Expiration Date _____ / _____
Mo   Yr

Please ship the "Career Handbook" @ $15.95 plus $4.00 for shipping.

Name _____

Address _____

City _____ State _____ Zip_____

THE ENGLISH HANDBOOK
OF
GRAMMAR, STYLE,
AND
COMPOSITION

- This book illustrates the rules and numerous exceptions that are characteristic of the English language, in great depth, detail, and clarity.

- Over 2,000 examples comparing correct and wrong usage in all areas of grammar and writing.

- Solves the usual confusion about punctuation.

- Illustrates spelling "tricks" and how to remember correct spelling.

- Teaches how to acquire good writing skills.

- Provides special learning exercises at the end of each chapter to prepare for homework and exams.

- Fully indexed for locating specific topics rapidly.

Available at your local bookstore or order directly from us by sending in coupon below.

HANDBOOK OF
MATHEMATICAL,
SCIENTIFIC, and
ENGINEERING
FORMULAS, TABLES,
FUNCTIONS, GRAPHS,
TRANSFORMS

A particularly useful reference for those in math, science, engineering and other technical fields. Includes the most-often used formulas, tables, transforms, functions, and graphs which are needed as tools in solving problems. The entire field of special functions is also covered. A large amount of scientific data which is often of interest to scientists and engineers has been included.

810

THE PROBLEM SOLVERS

The "PROBLEM SOLVERS" are comprehensive supplemental textbooks designed to save time in finding solutions to problems. Each "PROBLEM SOLVER" is the first of its kind ever produced in its field. It is the product of a massive effort to illustrate almost any imaginable problem in exceptional depth, detail, and clarity. Each problem is worked out in detail with step-by-step solution, and the problems are arranged in order of complexity from elementary to advanced. Each book is fully indexed for locating problems rapidly.

ADVANCED CALCULUS
ALGEBRA & TRIGONOMETRY
AUTOMATIC CONTROL
   SYSTEMS/ROBOTICS
BIOLOGY
BUSINESS, MANAGEMENT,
   & FINANCE
CALCULUS
CHEMISTRY
COMPLEX VARIABLES
COMPUTER SCIENCE
DIFFERENTIAL EQUATIONS
ECONOMICS
ELECTRICAL MACHINES
ELECTRIC CIRCUITS
ELECTROMAGNETICS
ELECTRONIC COMMUNICATIONS
ELECTRONICS
FINITE & DISCRETE MATH
FLUID MECHANICS/DYNAMICS
GENETICS

GEOMETRY:
PLANE · SOLID · ANALYTIC
HEAT TRANSFER
LINEAR ALGEBRA
MACHINE DESIGN
MECHANICS : STATICS · DYNAMICS
NUMERICAL ANALYSIS
OPERATIONS RESEARCH
OPTICS
ORGANIC CHEMISTRY
PHYSICAL CHEMISTRY
PHYSICS
PRE-CALCULUS
PSYCHOLOGY
STATISTICS
STRENGTH OF MATERIALS &
   MECHANICS OF SOLIDS
TECHNICAL DESIGN GRAPHICS
THERMODYNAMICS
TRANSPORT PHENOMENA :
MOMENTUM · ENERGY · MASS
VECTOR ANALYSIS

If you would like more information about any of these books, complete the coupon below and return it to us or go to your local bookstore.